Robert Davidson: Pioneer of Electric Locomotion

ROBERT DAVIDSON

Pioneer of Electric Locomotion

by Dr Antony Anderson

Published in 2018 by
The Grampian Transport Museum
Montgarrie Rd, Alford AB33 8AE

Book & cover design by Lumphanan Press
www.lumphananpress.co.uk

Printed and bound by
Imprint Digital, Exeter, Devon

ISBN: 978-1-5272-2014-0

Contents

Chapter One

Early Life in Aberdeen

ABERDEEN SEEMS TO HAVE FORGOTTEN ROBERT DAVIDSON. Perhaps one day a plaque will record that his crude experimental locomotive of 1842 predates by thirty-seven years Siemens' electric tramway at the Berlin Exhibition of 1879. Davidson is partly to blame for this lack of recognition, because he failed to document and publish his work, thinking, perhaps, that it would speak for itself. So we will have to pick our way as best we can, through scattered records, to piece together even the most approximate picture of the life of this enigmatic inventor.

Robert Davidson was born on 18 April 1804, the third child in a family of two boys and four girls. He died in 1894, so his life spanned a period of unprecedented change: At the time of his birth the Napoleonic Wars were in progress; he was a boy of eleven at the time of the Battle of Waterloo; as a young man he would have seen rapid industrialisation and the impact of the steam engine; in middle age he would have been able to send a telegraph to America or to India; in old age he would have been able to enjoy the benefits of electric light and the telephone.

His father, William Davidson, came from the small Aberdeen-shire village of Forgue, of a family of tenant farmers. In about 1795, he married Elizabeth Allardes, the sister of the likeable, but slightly eccentric, James Allardes of Forgue, the improving tenant farmer of Cobairdy. In 1814, by then well established in Aberdeen, William Davidson was elected a Burgess of the City of Aberdeen.

Nothing remains of the old Broad Street where William Davidson lived and had his shop. The original shop was almost opposite the Old Waterhouse; a building distinguished by a large clock tower and a reservoir[1] under which the town fire engines were kept. Close by was the tenement (No. 68) where Lord Byron spent some of his early years. Family legend has it that Byron used to buy sweetmeats in the Davidson shop. Later the shop was moved to 44 Broad Street, where it remained until it was pulled down to make way for the extensions to Marischal College in 1895.

In 1826 William Davidson, James Allardes and others founded the Glendronach Whisky Distillery, which is still operating and is now owned by the BenRiach Distillery Company. For ten years William Davidson was Secretary to the company. He pulled out of the partnership after the distillery had its second disastrous fire in 1836.

With his father William and his uncle James Allardes running a distillery, it is not surprising that young Robert should have developed an interest in chemistry, and that he should have turned his interest to yeast manufacture.

Another uncle, also called Robert Davidson, was a soapmaker.

This Robert was a man of some property and was, like his brother, a Burgess of Aberdeen.[2] He owned a large house near Elmfield, adjoining the Aberdeenshire Canal and bleach fields and a soap works in East Hutcheon Street. He died bankrupt in 1836 and his works – described in the Aberdeen Journal as 'extensive and the only soap works North of Leith of any considerable extent' – were sold to John Stewart, who set up the Aberdeen Comb works on the site.[3]

James Allardes, his maternal uncle, seems to have left a lasting impression on his contemporaries.[4,5,6,7,8,9] Indeed, much of his land improvement survives to this day: the casual observer surveying the farm of Cobairdy, near Forgue, with its protective belts of trees, would hardly realise that once it was a treeless, rock-strewn wilderness.

James Allardes was known as an enthusiastic land improver: draining and ditching his fields, building stone walls and planting trees. He was a cattle breeder too, not the best-known, but well thought of. His obituary[10] mentions his zeal in animating others to assist in the construction of the Forgue and Inverurie Turnpike, a road that linked the interior of the County of Aberdeenshire with the head of the Aberdeenshire Canal. He had an enthusiasm for progressive ventures. This is borne out by the risks that he and his associates must have taken in setting up a distillery. A different picture of him comes from the pen of the noted preacher, William Garden Blaikie, who met him in 1842. Allardes was by then an old man, bankrupt and almost an outcast.

> Amongst those who attended (the service) and seemed interested was a singular old gentleman whom everybody knew, for he was one of the 'characters' of the

neighbourhood. In his old age he kept up the dress of a past generation: knee breeches, blue coat and brass buttons, light coloured waistcoat and powdered hair. In former days, the Duke of Gordon, attracted by his eccentricity and quaint Scots dialect, used to have him much at Gordon Castle, and often did he speak of 'my particular friend the Duke of Gordon'.[11]

Good whisky and tall stories go together, and Glendronach has generated its fair share of improbable tales from the early days of the company. The founders, so the story goes,[12] had built the distillery and the still had been set going and the first whisky had been brewed and stored in bonds. Then the time came to sell the whisky. James Allardes sent out a traveller to comb the land for orders, but none were forthcoming. Thinking that he might do better himself, he set off to search for orders. He made no sales in Aberdeen but, undaunted, he sent off a big barrel of whisky to Edinburgh by sea and followed in his gig by road, carrying a flagon. When he got to Edinburgh, he found himself a good hotel and stored the flagon safely in his room before setting out to canvass the town. He went first to one public house and then to another, but made very few sales. He was walking up the Cannongate, when he was accosted by two young prostitutes, who with ideas of their own, asked him to give them a dram. Much to their surprise, James Allardes frog-marched the pair up the street, through the doors of the hotel, past some waiters – who thought the goings-on a little odd – and up the stairs to his room. There, he gave them each a full glass of whisky, which they drained.

'Tell yer friens,' he said, 'that ye hae got a dram o' the first Glendronach Whisky that was ever in Edinburgh.' He then got a waiter to bring him a bottle, which he filled with whisky, and gave it to them, saying: 'Tak it with ye an' treat yer friens.' Distanced somewhat from their cares, the women took their gift out into the street, where they began to imitate the accent and mannerisms of James Allardes in front of the passers-by. They finished the bottle, no doubt with a little help, and returned to the hotel to ask for more. To get past the waiters, they disguised themselves as respectable young ladies and presented themselves at James Allardes' door. By this time he had had quite enough of Edinburgh, because of the lack of sales, and in a gesture of resignation gave them the entire flagon; being resolved to head north for Aberdeen in the morning. Later that night a large, motley and intoxicated crowd gathered in the street asking for 'Guid Glendronach' and, thereafter, Glendronach was all the rage and the brand became well established in Edinburgh. Legend apart, to this day the whisky barrels at Glendronach are marked with the letters 'AL', for Allardes, and '1826' to indicate the year in which the distillery was opened.

Moving on to Robert Davidson's own generation: his older brother William passed through Marischal College three years ahead of him[13] and later became a partner in William Davidson and Son. More outgoing than Robert, he became a Burgess of the City. Mary Davidson, his sister, married William Connon, merchant of Aberdeen, who carried on the Davidson family business at 44 Broad Street after the deaths of William Davidson senior and junior.[14] Catherine, Isobel and Elizabeth, his other sisters, may have died young.[15]

✧

Like many of his contemporaries, Robert Davidson began his

schooling at 'Bodsie' Bowers' school in Long Acre.[16] Blaikie, who attended the school a few years after Robert Davidson wrote:

> Fancy a room like a ware-room perhaps twenty-five or thirty feet long, low in ceiling, with three or four small windows ill glazed and ill cleaned, the walls and roof begrimed with dust, the rough unwashed floor worn here and there into holes, suggesting excellent quarters for the rats below. The pupils, who were in various stages of advancement, were ranged in groups over the room, one group under the master, the rest professedly learning their lessons, but more probably engaged in the business which has always been found for idle hands to do. The noise was deafening, yet the energy of the master and the fear of the taws produced a greater measure of progress than might have been looked for. The dialect was the broadest, the tone of the school the roughest, and the behaviour of the boys to one another the rudest possible; and yet at the bottom there was a genuine kindliness and humanity that came out wonderfully if a boy met with an accident or fell into sickness.[17]

In later years Davidson was rather proud of reminding people that Lord Byron had been a pupil there some years before him. 'Bodsie' Bowers, from Byron's account, combined frequent punishment with unimaginative teaching:

> It was a school for both sexes. I learnt little except to repeat by rote the first lesson of monosyllables: 'God made man – let us love him.' [18]

From 'Bodsie' Bowers Davidson moved on for a while to a seminary in Broad Street and from there he moved to the Grammar School.

The Grammar School was then a plain, simple building of one storey in Schoolhill, with a small iron-railed playground in front. It was a grammar school in the original sense, where nothing else but Latin was taught.[19] Any other instruction had to be gained out of hours at other establishments, which were also under the City Authorities. Blaikie,[20] writing of the Grammar School writes:

> The schoolroom was arranged in parallel rows of seats, like the pews of a church, four boys in each row, with a passage between; and the seats, for what cause I know not, were called 'factions'. It was highly honourable to be in the first faction, creditable to be in the second, respectable in the third, but deplorable to be in the fourth or lowest. We had a class of seventy or eighty, of whom three of four were always contending for the highest place. Certainly this rivalry stimulated our efforts; even the division into factions had marked effect. I do not think the rivalry had evil in it, for the faction boys were usually warm friends and congenial companions.

> The manners of the school were singularly rough. Before the master entered, there would be a very Babel of noise – boys running over the tops of the seats, tugging and tearing at one another, or thumping on the seats with their fists or their books… The games were of the simplest and most inexpensive description: the

playground in front of the school was but a few square yards, but it was a scene of extraordinary animation and noise, and I think that we were quite as happy with our peg-tops and peeries, our handballs, marbles and buttons, as if we had had a magnificent field for cricket or football...with all the rough manners, there was little bitterness of feeling; and though a fight or duel between two boys was very popular when it did occur, this was rather from the love of excitement or the love of the scene than any coarser feeling. The discipline of the school depended much on the tawse; its strokes were invariably called 'pandies' from pando, I stretch out, but the master whose influence was greatest had seldom occasion to resort to it. Great offences used, at one time, to be punished in the public school before the whole assembled pupils, the culprit being mounted on the back of the janitor, but this revolting and indecent punishment in the public school had ceased before my time.

ప

The concentration on Latin at the Grammar School mentioned earlier was partly a tradition, but, more importantly, because the school was one of the main feeders for the two universities of Aberdeen. Kings College and Marischal College each had about twenty public bursaries open to competition each October. The competition for bursaries was solely an exercise in translating a piece of English prose into Latin; hence the premium placed upon a mastery of that language.

In his article 'Dead men I have known' David Masson writes:

The bursaries were of small amounts, ranging from £5 a year to £20 a year; but invariably, by the terms of the foundation, each bursary more than covered all the expenses of the college classes. Now it was this Bursary System – as familiarly known over the whole region concerned as the Aurora Borealis in its nightly sky – it was this Bursary System that had generated and that had sustained there a habit of looking forward to a University education amongst classes in which otherwise such a habit could hardly have been possible. Though the well-to-do youths in the town or in the country around might not care for a bursary – save for the honour – and it was reputed an honour, and when obtained, was kept as such by many to whom it could have been of no substantial consideration, yet for a scholarly boy of poor family in one of the third rate streets of Aberdeen, or from a poor farmer's son on Donside, following his father's plough and dreaming of a college life as the furrow came to the field's edge, the thought that would murmur to his lips would still be: 'A Bursary; O for a Bursary.' With many their going or not going to college depended on their winning or not winning, at the proper time, this coveted prize. One can see what influence such an agency might have been made to exercise over the schooling and intellectual activity of the region within which it operated. [21]

So it was that boys of all social classes, rich and poor, came to the Grammar School; hoping eventually to win one of these bursaries. While to us the concentration on Latin seems strange, yet the result was that opportunity was available to many people, of a kind that in many places has not been matched even to this day.

Robert Davidson passed in to Marischal College, Aberdeen at the age of fourteen[22] – the usual age at that time – and remained there for the next six years, which was a somewhat longer period than usual. He was not one of the lucky bursary winners, but even so, the outlay for his father would have been small.

At that time, there were two universities in Aberdeen. Students from the Highlands and North, and those with a bias towards classics favoured King's College in Old Aberdeen. Students, like Davidson, who sought a more practical training – engineers, clockmakers and artisans – favoured Marischal College.[23] Marischal College drew its students from Aberdeen itself, the eastern and lowland parts of Aberdeenshire, Kincardineshire and Forfarshire (the county of Angus). One of Davidson's contemporaries at Marischal was Alexander Gibb, the civil engineer and one time assistant to Thomas Telford; he was the son of John Gibb, the lessee of the Rubislaw Granite Quarry.

The A.M. degree course lasted four years. The curriculum was wide in its scope, including Greek, Latin, Theology, Mathematics and Natural Philosophy. The classes were open to anyone, there being about equal numbers of regular and extramural students. The latter could attend classes more or less as they wished. There was no compulsion to complete the degree, and a check of the records for the years 1818–24 shows that out of a class of 99 students, about one third graduated A.M.

Two things stand out clearly: firstly, the students came from a far wider background than would have been the case in an English university at that time, largely because of the bursary system; secondly, some practical knowledge was an integral part of the arts degree.

Marischal College, prior to its rebuilding, has been described by David Masson[24] one of its old students as that:

> massive old pile in the great space of ground entered by the old gateway from the Broadgate ... impressive by its amorphous gray massiveness even in daylight, but in winter-nights quite weirdly to look at in the dark space that enshrined it, with the few lights twinkling in one of its small windows ... and then the classrooms as we sat in them by day – all old and quaint, though some older and quainter than others and the great common hall stretching the whole width of the main building in the first storey, with its old chimney piece in the middle, on which were carved the arms of the Earl Marischal with their noble motto of scorn for public opinion ('Aiunt: Quid aiunt? Aiunt.' In English: 'They say; What say they? Let them say!').

The student would have studied Greek and Humanity (Latin) in the first session, and in the second he would have widened their studies to include Mathematics and Natural History. The mathematics course was given by Professor Robert Hamilton,[25] who had acquired a considerable reputation as an economist. He was timid, absent minded and short-sighted: the perfect target for projectiles. He was much loved because, for all the provocation, he never bore the instigators any ill will. Many stories are told about him, most apocryphal. He is said, on one occasion, to have stumbled against a cow on the links and to have said, on passing his wife shortly afterwards: 'is that you again brute?' There is no record of his wife's reply.

Natural History, the main second year course, was given by

Dr James Davidson, the Professor of Natural and Civil History. His lectures were said to be very entertaining, although possibly more for the students than for him. He began by explaining the ideas of the ancients about the nature and properties of matter and moved on to cover the historical development of alchemy and its effect on the growth of science. He described the elements in their three forms – solid, liquid and gaseous – and their various natural and man-made combinations. His course was therefore more of an introduction to chemistry than it was to natural philosophy.

On two days of the week he illustrated his lecture subject matter by experiment, using materials that he kept in a little closet attached to the classroom. Keen students looked forward to these experimental days and, for the rest of the class, they offered a splendid opportunity to let off steam. James Riddell[26], writes:

> His first set of experiments, I remember, was intended to illustrate the distinctive properties of acid and alkalis and their different effects on vegetable colours. Some irreverent youth had (years before I was at College) characterised the vegetable solutions thus operated on as 'Cabbage Bree', a designation handed down from one generation of the Doctor's students to another. So when he happened at any time throughout his course of experiments to be occupied in the illustration of a subject less interesting than that referred to, he would be saluted by some one or other of the 'black sheep' in the class saying, in feigned voice: 'That's nae worth, duketer, gie us yer cabbage bree.'

Not all of his experiments worked and he attributed their failure to dampness in the closet, much to the merriment of the class. Practical jokers wet his candles so that they went out, or they would embed glass bombs, which then exploded with the heat of the flame, causing a lot of noise and distraction. In other words, Dr Davidson and his class were in a state of incessant, riotous warfare.

In the third session, the student would have taken Natural Philosophy in the class of Patrick Copland, Professor of Natural Philosophy from 1817–22. One of Copland's old pupils described him as 'the most efficient of the public teachers of Marischal College.'[27] He was the first professor in the North of Scotland to give a course of a simple and popular nature on mechanics, which was suitable for the mechanic and the operative tradesman. His mechanical equipment comprised the best collection of models in the land at that time. It was all made either by him or by workmen that he had trained himself. He was the first person in Great Britain to make a serious attempt to teach by means of demonstration models. His other claim to distinction was to have introduced chlorine bleaching into Scotland independently and contemporaneously with James Watt, following a visit that he made to De Saussure in Geneva with the Duke of Gordon in 1787.[28,29,30]

'Robert Davidson,' we are told, 'was enabled to stay longer than usual at the University on account of the assistance that he rendered to one of the professors, by providing a model engine of his own construction for demonstration purposes in one of the classes.'[31] This probably was a steam engine and it could have been made either for Copland or his successor, William Knight. By this time, Davidson's mechanical abilities seem to have been well developed and appreciated by those who knew him.

Copland's use of working models must have made an impression on the students: we may sense an influence on Davidson, who later chose to communicate with the public through working models and exhibitions, rather than through the written word.

Copland died in 1822 and William Knight took over the class, following, as far as one can tell, somewhat similar lines to Copland. He covered Mechanics, Hydrostatics, Magnetism, Optics and Astronomy. As time went on, he added Electromagnetism to the course.

Knight was a careful lecturer, and wrote his notes neatly in octavo notebooks, with blank spaces left for later additions.[32,33] His knowledge was broad, but his mathematics was shallow.

> His course was one rather of rich and miscellaneous descriptive information than of mathematical investigation and demonstration. He introduced formulae and calculations now and then; but his lectures were rather like an exceedingly interesting and well-arranged scientific encyclopaedia for moderate mathematical readers.[34]

For anyone who wished to use it, there was a library of standard books on natural philosophy attached to the class. To keep the students on their toes, Knight demanded an essay each week on a subject recently discussed in the class and he fined those who made a late submission; but whether he read the fifty or so essays that he collected each week is open to conjecture.

Knight must have seemed a strange and complex man to his contemporaries. On the one hand, he was a stickler for authority and rules; with this went a strong temper and a very sarcastic tongue. On the other hand, he was an excellent companion; kind to his students and showing them more familiarity than most of the other professors. [35] Beneath the conservative lay the radical, who wanted his students to think for themselves. 'Use your reason,' he would urge them. 'You are told every day not to use your reason; do it for all that.'[36] David Masson, one of his former students, writes:

> In truth, I believe that Knight lived and walked in Aberdeen in a perpetual relation of secret irony to everything about him and especially to popular and clerical opinion.[37]

Knight's students would soon forget the facts that he taught them and his sharp tongue, but they retained the habits of thought and constructive speculation which he imparted to them. Knight made his mark in student folklore, and one story in particular gives a measure of the man. It was his custom to follow the common academic practice of prefacing the daily business of the class with a prayer; either the Lord's Prayer or one of his own. When praying, he had the disconcerting habit of keenly scrutinising his class, a custom not exactly designed to turn his class towards the path of true religion. On one occasion, a student slipped in to the classroom unobserved, or so he thought, just as the Lord's Prayer was coming to an end. Knight, without the slightest change in tempo, finished the prayer thus: 'For thine is the Kingdom, the Power and the Glory for ever. Amen. You're late, you brute!'[38]

Robert Davidson would have learned some chemistry in the second year from James Davidson, but it is likely that he attended the Chemistry class, then nominally given by Professor French, but in practice mostly taken by Dr William Henderson.

French was old-fashioned and he certainly did not hold with Sir Humphrey Davy on the constitution of salts. For example, he would not have considered common salt to be a compound of the two elements sodium and chlorine, but a compound of an acid oxide and a basic oxide. He was fond of saying to his students:

> There's a man of the name of Davy who is now telling us that this is all wrong. He is a troublesome man, Mr Davy, but we'll bide a wee till we see. [39]

Fortunately, Henderson, his deputy, was more modern in his views.

The course syllabus was as follows:

> The power by which substances act chemically upon one another is explained and its effects illustrated by experiments; the different chemical operations are explained, directions given for performing them, and illustrated by experiments; the nature and effect of caloric, or heat, explained and illustrated by experiment; the principal processes connected with the different branches of Chemistry, as connected with saline substances, metals, earths are actually performed in the class on moderate quantities of materials; Phosphorus and Ether are prepared; The application of chemistry to arts, manufactures, pharmacy and agriculture, so far as concerns the examination of soils is pointed out in the course. [40]

The Chemistry class met for one hour on three days of the week during the five months of the college session. The same class was repeated year after year and the students were expected to attend the course for two successive years: 'because they are supposed, in the first course not to understand very well, but to understand very much better in the second year.'[41] In practice, very few students attended the second time round. At that time, the students did no experimental work. Keen students must therefore have carried out experiments elsewhere, unsupervised, with chemicals that they could buy in small quantities from the chemist's shop.

So we see that by the age of twenty, Robert Davidson had received a sound general education, with an emphasis on science and the useful arts. The knowledge he must have gained seems rather elementary by the standards of today, but in a gifted student it was sufficient to encourage further study and experiment.

Either during his time at Marischal College, or more probably shortly afterwards, Robert Davidson went on a tour of the continental battlefields with a friend called Ronald Macdonald.[42] They stayed at an inn near the battlefield, where Wellington and Blucher had met, and they were offered the skulls of fallen soldiers by the local inhabitants as souvenirs.

For a while Davidson worked in his father's grocery business, but this really did not interest him. Customers often made enquiries for yeast: he began to experiment and soon was able to brew it for them. He was so successful at this that he set up his own business. We may presume that a major customer would have been the Glendronach Distillery, which opened in 1826. He amassed what was then a fortune from brewing yeast before giving it up and turning his mind to other things.

❧

Whisky

The history of attempts by the Government to regulate the distilling of whisky is long and complicated. Illegal stills and smuggling were commonplace. It was not until 1823, largely as a result of an initiative taken by the 4th Duke of Gordon, that legislation was introduced that eventually caused the disappearance of the illicit distiller and the smuggler.

The Duke of Gordon, who owned large tracts of land in the north-east of Scotland, argued in the House of Lords that you could not stop the Highlander from distilling. However, if sensible legislation were to be introduced to provide favourable conditions for the legal manufacture of whisky, then he and his fellow landed proprietors would do their best to suppress illicit distilling and encourage their tenants to take out licences for stills.

The 1823 Act sanctioned the distilling of whisky on payment of duty of 2s.3d. per gallon of proof spirit and payment of a licence fee of £10 on all stills with a capacity of 40 gallons or more.

The Glendronach Distillery was therefore one amongst a number of distilleries that were set up shortly after the passing of the 1823 Act, with the direct encouragement of the Duke of Gordon. The distillery would probably have met with some local opposition and it is possible that the two fires that occurred in the early years were not accidental.

Initially the 1823 Act encouraged the development of good legal distilleries and reduced illicit distilling and smuggling. However, by 1830 the tax had been raised to 3s. 4d. and, in consequence, illicit distilling and smuggling were once more on the rise. The legal distillers found themselves facing increased competition: to meet the challenge, they sold their whisky new, without waiting for it to mature.

So we see that William Davidson's decision to relinquish his share in the business in 1836 may not have been solely on account of the fire, but also because of falling profitability of whisky distilling. Similarly, Robert Davidson's expansion from the manufacture of yeast to chemicals may have been the result of finding that there was a falling market for yeast.

Chapter Two

File Manufacturer and Manufacturing Chemist

ABERDEEN IN THE 1830S WAS A GROWING AND BUSTLING CITY of 60,000 inhabitants. Somewhat isolated by land, it thrived on its seaborne trade. Ships of all kinds might be found in the harbour: small coastal vessels bringing coal from Wallsend on Tyne; whaling ships from Arctic waters, bringing sperm oil to light the lamps; trading vessels unloading cargoes from Baltic ports, or sometimes India and the Far East; and other ships Canada-bound bound for Halifax, Pictou and Miramachi.

Aberdeen was a city of industry: there were shipyards, iron foundries and brass foundries, woollen mills and cotton mills. In short, there were ample opportunities in the city for a young man to turn his knowledge of practical chemistry to profitable account, there being, as yet, no substantial competition for business from chemical manufacturers based in the South.

Robert Davidson began the manufacture of colouring dyes at

the Aberdeen Colouring Works, Causeway End[43] and – from about 1832 onwards – at Canal Road.[44] Here he managed, after some difficulty, to purchase a large feu.[45] The Canal Road site adjoined the Aberdeenshire Canal, the main link to the interior of the county, which provided a supply of water and cheap transport, both inland to Inverurie and to the Port of Aberdeen.

We may trace Davidson's activities through the occasional advertisements that he placed in the Aberdeen Journal. For instance, on 10 August 1831 we read the following:

TO PAINTERS AND DRYSALTERS

ROBERT DAVIDSON returns thanks to those who have favoured him with their commands since he commenced business as **PRUSSIAN BLUE** and **COLOUR MANU-FACTURER**, and begs to assure the Trade in general that his articles are of the first quality, and are sold on the lowest terms. **LIQUID BLUE**, for **BLEACHERS – LONDON** and **FRESH BARM**, as formerly.

Aberdeen Colour Works, Causewayend.

One of his customers was Hadden's Woollen Mill on the Green, whom he supplied for over half a century. Another was Stewart's Comb Works, whom he provided with chemicals for staining purposes.[46]

Stewart's represents a typical example of industrial expansion in Aberdeen, and Davidson's fortunes must have been bound up with and were favoured by this growth. The firm was founded, with forty hands, somewhere about 1831.[47] In 1836 the comb works moved to the site previously occupied by the soapworks of Robert Davidson's uncle.[48] By 1854, the factory was turning out nine million combs a year. Some idea of the scale of the operation can be gauged from the following: up to 100,000 horns were used each week, as well as vast quantities of hoof, tortoiseshell and vulcanite. About 1600 tons of waste products were collected each year and were sold to fertiliser manufacturers, who used it to make up their manures.

Industry today is highly specialised, but this was not so in the 1830s. Davidson seems to have followed the winds of fortune, or perhaps his own fancy. On 15 August 1831, we find the following advertisement in the Aberdeen Journal: [49]

FILE CUTTING

ROBERT DAVIDSON begs to intimate to engine Makers, Smiths and Workers in Metal generally that he has begun the Business of **FILE CUTTING** in Aberdeen; and, from having brought experienced tradesmen from Sheffield, he trusts that any work committed to his charge will be executed to the satisfaction of his employees. R.D. intends, in the meantime, to devote his attention to the **RE-CUTTING OF OLD FILES**, which, upon trial, will be found to be as good as new.

N.B. Wanted, a person who has been accustomed to grind Metal and keep a Stove.

☙

The cutting and sharpening of files has to be carried out in a well-equipped machine shop. Heat-treating the files to harden them requires a sound knowledge of chemistry in order to prepare the temperature-indicating coatings that must be put onto the files before they are hardened. So this advertisement indicates that Davidson was now more than a manufacturing chemist and could be better described as a general mechanical engineer. The reason, probably, for this diversification is that in those days there were very few specialist machinery manufacturers and therefore, if you needed a machine, you made it yourself. There are numerous examples of nineteenth-century engineers who were, by today's standards, very versatile and took a pride in being able to tackle anything: making virtue out of a necessity. Davidson was cast in this same mould: the lathes that he used in his workshop were driven by a steam engine that he built himself.[50] His obituary suggests that he could turn his hand to anything and says that he practised for a while as a dentist! It was necessary for Davidson to be a jack-of-all-trades, yet this same versatility may have been his undoing. For the ability to appreciate all the possibilities that life presents may also take the edge off the determination to pursue any one objective to the bitter end. But then, perhaps this would be an unfair judgment, because although he initially made big profits as a yeastmaker, he did not do so for long. As this advertisement indicates,[51] he soon had some strong competition:

YEAST FOR DISTILLERS

The **SUBSCRIBERS** beg leave to intimate
a considerable fall in the price of **LONDON
YEAST**, which article they continue to
supply, of very best quality, either direct from
London, or from their Store at Aberdeen, as
may be required. Also, that they have lately
commenced the **MANUFACTURE of FRESH
YEAST**, The quality and efficiency of which,
for starting the Fermenting Tuns, they can
warrant. Price moderate, and sent out in such
quantities as may be wanted.
STEWART & RUTHERFORD
Crown Court,
Aberdeen, 27th March 1832.

Davidson may have decided that he did not have the resources to
match this competition from the south and so withdrew to less
contested ground.

This industrial activity would be enough for most men, but
not for Davidson.

Young Davidson was a lover of astronomy and one
of his favourite hobbies was the construction of
telescopes. At first he contented himself with small
things, but after making a number of telescopes of
ordinary size, he set himself to the construction of an

instrument of large dimensions. The work was long and difficult, but the young man applied to it persevering industry and surmounting all obstacles completed the instrument in 1828 when in his 24th year. The telescope was ... of large size having a length of 35 feet and a corresponding diameter. It was fitted up on a platform on the grounds at Canal Road and for many years it was a source of great pleasure to the constructor and others to survey the heavens through its powerful magnifiers. [52]

This is probably the same telescope that Robert Rettie saw in 1836,[53] which had a reflecting speculum of two feet in diameter. Little information has come to light about the telescope which, on account of its size, must have been something of a local landmark. There seem to be no extant descriptions of it at all. All that was left of it by the 1890s were a few lenses, and some dilapidated sections of the huge tube. Who knows, perhaps even today the lenses are in use somewhere, their provenance being unsuspected. If they were of reasonable quality, it is unlikely that they would have been destroyed. In addition to this interest in astronomy, Davidson developed an interest in electricity and magnetism, which became his main interest from 1837 onwards.

Summarising, Davidson spent the years from 1824 to 1837 in three ways: firstly, building up his business as a manufacturing chemist; secondly, in general engineering activities like file manufacture; thirdly, on his hobbies of astronomy and later electromagnetism.

He must have funded his electromagnetic experiments with the profits from his business, which would not have been difficult so long as he was living in Aberdeen and could keep a close eye on his affairs. However, any long absence would have meant delegating the day to day running of the business to others, with all the attendant risks of loss, and it explains his initial reluctance to leave his native city. That he was later able to spend two years away from Aberdeen without his business collapsing is a measure both of the sound state that he must have left it in and the degree of support given to him by his family. Had he been married at this time, he would have had less time for experiment and would have had other demands upon his purse and possibly his ideas would never have seen the light of day.

Chapter Three

Early Experiments in Electromagnetism

WE SAW IN THE LAST CHAPTER HOW ROBERT DAVIDSON HAD established a successful business as a manufacturing chemist by the mid 1830s and that by 1837 electromagnetism was his main hobby interest. He made his first electric motor in that year and he experimented for the next two years. By 1839, he had made sufficient progress to have some working machines that he could show privately to the Rev. Professor Patrick Forbes and others.

There is no evidence to suggest that Davidson was interested in electromagnetism before 1837, nor do we know what sparked off his interest. The Rev. Nicholas Callan,[54] the inventor of the induction coil, and the English physicist James Prestcott Joule, who both made important contributions to the development of electromagnetism, came from families of brewers and distillers,[55] as did Davidson. There appears to be a natural progression here: brewers might be expected to have an interest in practical chemistry and would pass some of this interest on to members of their immediate family; chemistry leads to electrochemistry; electrochemistry finds its natural extension in electromagnetism. On the other hand, Davidson's enthusiasm may have been fired by any of the following: his own circle of friends; the Aberdeen Mechanic's Institute, or visiting lecturers in electromagnetism; or articles in the Mechanic's Magazine. Nor should it be forgotten that one of the best-known and most effective early experimenters in electromagnetism was the Rev. William Ritchie of University College London and the Royal Institution. Ritchie was a graduate of Marischal College,[56] and may be presumed to have retained some links with his native city and the small circle of those individuals there interested in science.

To try to understand the circumstances in which it was both possible and natural for Davidson and others to become interested in electromagnetism, let us go back to the year 1820. In that year, the Danish scientist H. C. Oersted discovered the link between electricity and magnetism that had long been sought but which had proved so elusive.[57] He placed a freely suspended magnet close to a wire carrying an electric current and found that the magnet took up a new position the moment that the current was switched on. By this means he demonstrated that an electric current flowing in a wire produced a magnetic effect that was similar to that produced by the Earth's field. The news of Oersted's experiment caused great excitement in the scientific world. The experiment was repeated elsewhere and the results were verified. This in turn led to new discoveries and to the establishment of the fundamental laws of electromagnetism and, eventually, to its practical application.

In 1821 Michael Faraday, the English experimental chemist, managed to get a suspended wire carrying a current to rotate continuously about a magnet.[58] The apparatus was little more than a philosophical toy, but it demonstrated the fundamental principles of an electric motor – that a force is exerted on a current-carrying conductor in a magnetic field – and stimulated others to attempt to make devices that were more practical.

Schweiger of Halle found that he could amplify the magnetic field of a long straight wire by winding the same wire round a former as a multi-turn coil or helix.[59] The magnetic effect was shown to depend on the magnitude of the current, the number of turns in the coil and its dimensions. It was soon found that iron filings were drawn into the magnetic field,[60] and from this it was a comparatively short step to the discovery by William Sturgeon that iron could increase the magnetic effect of the current. He embodied this principle in his electromagnet of 1824. He bent an iron bar into a horseshoe and varnished it and then wound sixteen turns of bare copper wire upon the horseshoe. With this magnet he was able to suspend a weight of nine pounds and demonstrated that large forces could be produced between an electromagnet and its keeper, or armature, so long as the distances between the two were kept small. Sturgeon was awarded a silver medal and purse of thirty guineas by the Society of Arts in 1825 for his invention.[61]

For some unknown reason, Sturgeon does not seem to have thought of winding on more than one layer of wire, and this improvement we owe to the American Joseph Henry with whom Sturgeon communicated, who took up Sturgeon's ideas and developed them. Henry managed to achieve a balance between the quantity of copper in the electric circuit and the amount of iron in the magnetic circuit by winding many layers of insulated wire over a short, fat, horseshoe-shaped core.

Henry's magnets were extremely effective. By 1831 he had built a 59-pound magnet that could support a weight of nearly a ton. In the same year, one of his magnets was put to industrial use for the separation of iron ore at Ironville, N.Y. – the very first practical application of electromagnetism,[62] and a hint of what was to come. Oddly enough, the lessons of good magnet design that could be learned from Henry were lost on most of his contemporaries and their successors, who tended[63] to make their magnets long and thin. This false line of reasoning was embodied in Edison's 'Long-waisted Mary Ann' generator as late as 1879. Some early electromagneticians, William Ritchie and M. M. Jacobi among them, seem to have had an intuitive grasp of the principles of good magnet design.[64] Others, such as Callan, seem to have kept close to Sturgeon's original horseshoe and scaled it up.

Seeing that electromagnets could produce large attractive forces for so small a consumption of zinc in a battery, inventors and scientists began to reason that these same forces might be harnessed to produce continuous motion: but how? By itself, the electromagnet could produce a large, short-range force on a piece of iron or upon a current-carrying conductor, but not continuous motion. It took six years from the publication of Sturgeon's invention before the once-only attraction of the electromagnet was converted into continuous motion.[65] It was a further two years before Sturgeon demonstrated in public the raising of weights by an electric motor.[66]

The key lay in combining the electromagnet with a second device – a switch or commutator – which switched the current on and off, as and when the armature was in the correct positions relative to the electromagnet. As soon as the current was switched on, the armature was attracted to the electromagnet.

When the movement had been completed, the current was switched off. This removed the large force holding the armature fast on the poles of the electromagnet and allowed the armature to be moved effortlessly to a new position, from where the whole cycle of attraction could be repeated. Without the make-and-break action of the switch, the energy in the magnetic field is trapped and there can be no continuous conversion of electrical into mechanical energy.

In the early 1830s a variety of simple electric motors appeared: some were oscillating motors, others were rotary motors; some had electromagnets on both the stationary and rotating members of the motor, others had electromagnets on only one machine member and a set of permanent magnets or plain iron bars on the other. At first, motion was considered a sufficient end in itself but, as the decade went on, the emphasis changed to obtaining power with economy. Motors and batteries improved slowly and each new improvement in the one acted as an incentive to improve the other.

The problems facing would-be electromagneticians at that time were formidable, because they would have to make almost everything themselves. To make a tolerably good battery, they needed a knowledge of chemistry. The twin phenomena of local electrolytic action and gas polarisation[67] troubled early battery constructors and made the conversion of chemical into electrical energy needlessly inefficient. Local action, which could dissipate up to three-quarters of the available battery energy within the cells as heat, was caused by tiny electrolytic cells which formed on the surface of the electrodes at the sites of local impurities. After each use of the battery the plates had to be taken out of the electrolyte and cleaned. De la Rive showed that electrodes made from pure zinc were not affected by local action, but because pure zinc was very expensive, the use of zinc plates was not a practical solution. Fortunately, Davy discovered shortly afterwards that the same effect could be produced at a fraction of the cost by amalgamating the surface of an impure zinc electrode with mercury.[68]

Gas polarisation, which led to a substantial rise in the internal resistance of the cell as long as current was drawn from it, was also a problem. It was caused by the blocking action of small bubbles of hydrogen gas liberated at the electrodes. Daniell[69] largely overcame the problem by using two separate solutions of electrolyte, which were separated by a porous membrane. This led to the rapid development of other types of cells, most of which worked on similar principles.

Even supposing that our would-be electromagneticians managed to make batteries that were leak-tight and that the fumes given off did not overcome them, they still needed some mechanical skill to build their motors – unless, like Charles Wheatstone, they were wealthy enough to afford the services of a skilled instrument maker like William Henley.[70]

The difficulties of making a motor that worked at all will be appreciated when we realise that the modern electrical machine designer uses a very high level of mathematical and computational skill.[71] No such help was available in the 1830s. Although Ohm's Law – relating electromotive force, current and circuit resistance – was first published in 1827,[72] it remained unknown in Great Britain until the late 1830s.

The Magnetic Circuit Law (analogous to Ohm's Law for electric circuits) would remain unknown for many years, although anyone reading a paper written by William Ritchie in 1832[73] would have seen that some law ought to exist, although its precise form was indeterminate. Machine constructors were

guided more by conjecture and trial and error than by an understanding of fundamental principles.

Before the invention of the simple screw terminal, which
forces conductors into direct metal-to-metal contact, experimenters were plagued by poor contacts. Often connections were
made via little cups of mercury, which could be upset by either
movement or vibration. Mercury was also used in reversing
switches, commutators and to amalgamate battery surfaces.
Since no special precautions were taken, many experimenters
must have suffered from temporary sickness or even long-term
brain damage from mercury vapour poisoning.

There were few artificial insulating materials – no plastics or
rubbers[74] – and much use was made of wood, ivory and silk.[75]
Obtaining insulated wire for winding the coils of an electromagnet was often difficult and expensive. This letter, printed in
Sturgeon's Annals of Electricity, illustrates the point:

> Sir,
> The enormous price charged by the opticians for cov-
> ered copper wire and a desire to diminish as much as
> possible the expense of electromagnetic studies induces
> me to inform your readers how they may get it cheaper.
> Those who cover bonnet wire charge only about 6d
> per pound; it is only necessary then to discover a wire
> coverer and supply him with the copper wire, as thus it
> will not cost one third of the optician's charge...
> With best wishes for the continued success of your
> excellent Annals,
> I remain, Yours respectfully,
> G. Francis [76]

By the late 1830s, the problem of material supply was beginning to lessen because, by then, the number of amateur electricians had increased, and there was a market for a whole range of items – from insulated copper wire to bar magnets – which philosophical instrument makers, platina and tinsmiths and the like were ready to supply.

So let us now look in greater detail at the progress in electric motors between 1831 and 1837, the year in which we will take up Davidson's story.

Joseph Henry built an oscillating motor in 1831.[77] Salvatore Dal Negro of the University of Padua also built one at about the same time which, with the aid of a mechanical linkage, was able to lift 60 grams through a height of five centimetres in one second.[78] William Sturgeon was lifting small weights with a rotary motor in 1832 and was demonstrating the motor in the following year.[79] By 1833, William Ritchie was entertaining audiences at the Royal Institution with a wide variety of interesting electromagnetic toys.[80] His motor was copied widely and might often be seen in the windows of philosophical instrument makers. At about the same time '.',[81] an anonymous Irish correspondent of the Mechanic's Magazine, described a form of stepping motor which had a two-pole stator and an eight-pole permanent magnet rotor. We would have heard more of '.' had he and a party of his friends not been drowned shortly afterwards while boating on Lough Strang.

By 1834, M. M. Jacobi, a brother of the better-known mathe-matician, was at the time working at Koenigsberg in Prussia, and was lifting weights of 20 ounces. A little later he was reporting that his improved motor had an output, measured by prony brake, of between ten and twelve foot pounds per second.[82, 83]

Meanwhile in America, Thomas Davenport, an untutored

blacksmith from Vermont, had been so impressed by the ability of one of Henry's magnets to separate iron ore that he bought it for his own use.[84] Proceeding by trial and error, he managed to build a small motor incorporating the magnet, which had a seven-inch flywheel and which rotated at about 30 rpm.[85]

We can gauge the interest in electromagnetism in Scotland at this time from an advertisement placed in the Dundee Advertiser on 13 April 1834 by James Bowman Lindsay, lecturer at the Watt Institute:[86]

> In a few weeks hence a course of lectures will be formed on frictional, galvanic and voltaic electricity; magnetism; and electromagnetism. The battery, already powerful, is undergoing daily augmentation. The light obtained from it is intensely bright, and the number of lights may be increased without limit. A great number of wheels may be turned by electricity and small weights raised over pulleys. Houses will in a short time be lighted by electricity instead of gas, and heated by it instead of coal; and machinery will be worked by it instead of steam – all at trifling expense. A miniature view of all these effects will be exhibited, besides a number of subordinate experiments including the discoveries of Sir Humphrey Davy.

In America, Davenport was continuing his experiments, with some success. But in spite of a flair for catching the attention of the press, he was finding it difficult to get financial support. News of his work reached Great Britain in 1837, where it caused great interest. The Mechanic's Magazine carried its first report in July that year[87] and thereafter continued to keep its readers informed of his progress.

Robert Chambers, editor of the Edinburgh Journal, thought that the possibilities of electromagnetism as a motive power would interest his general readership and he reprinted the same American article on Davenport. In his preface, he struggles to explain the unfamiliar concepts of electromagnetism to his readers:

> The electromagnetic power is evolved at the most trifling expense by means of an apparatus called a battery, consisting of two boxes with plates of metal standing upright in them, the interstices between the plates being filled with an acidulous liquid. From each box a wire proceeds, and this wire carries the electric or magnetic property, which is mysteriously evolved in the boxes, and by its action on leaving the wires gives a magnetic property to iron or, according as it may be applied, motion to a revolving bar or needle fixed to a spindle. A strap from the spindle, as a matter of course, turns any machinery that it is connected with.[88]

Chambers' article would have been widely read. It is therefore reasonable to suppose that knowledge of Davenport's achievements, but not the detail of his motor designs, would have been widespread in Scotland by mid 1837 and that this would have quickened the interest of anyone whose thoughts were already turning in this direction.

Davenport's motors continued to attract attention. His electromagnetic roundabout was exhibited at the Adelaide Gallery in London in 1838 and great care was taken to hide the working mechanism.[89] On Saturday 18 January 1840 he printed the first number of the Electromagnetic and Mechanic's Intelligencer on a printing press driven by one of his own motors.[90] Davenport thought big – he wanted to build a large boat driven by an electric motor, but he spoilt his case for financial support by his wild assertion that:

> half a barrel of blue Vitriol and a hogshead or two of water would send a ship from New York to Liverpool.

One sympathetic correspondent, who had done some calculations to check Davenport's claim, put it:

> I smiled when I read this assertion, such powers appeared to me as surpassing magic itself and this was the cause of my making the aforesaid calculations and soon convinced me that Mr Davenport himself had not made any calculations on the subject, but had been influenced by hope and guided by conjecture.[91]

Although Davenport let his enthusiasm run away with him and never quite matched achievement to hope, he strongly influenced the utilitarian expectations that people held for electromagnetic power, as we can see from the following speculative paragraphs from the Franklin Journal for January 1838:

> If we hire a man by the day we must not allow him to be idle, as in that case we give our money for nothing. The current of his life flows on, and he must be fed and clothed or the stream will stop. But give us a machine which is not costly at first, and which if it works but

one hour in the twenty-four, will itself be a consumer in that proportion only; a machine which we can at any moment set to turn our lathes, our grindstones, our washing machines, our churns, our circular saws, and a catalogue of other things which it would be no easy task to make out; such a machine would also perform a million of other operations by the conversion of the rotary into a reciprocating motion; and we again ask who is there among us who would not want one? Our farmers, our mechanics, and our housekeepers generally must all be supplied. We could no more submit to live without it, after it had been introduced than we can now submit to travel at the slow rate of ten miles an hour, an event we have learnt to think one of the miseries of life. With such a machine at our command we should wonder how we could have lived so long without it; and if taken from us it would leave a most awful chasm in the necessaries of life, the existence of which our fathers never dreamed, and happily we could not be called upon to witness so long as the store house of nature would enable us to obtain zinc and sulphuric acid at a cheap rate.

Let it not be said that we are prophesying about what is going to happen; not so by any means; but be it remembered that we are speaking of what is a possible contingency. we have no doubt respecting the practicability of obtaining the power of a man by the agency of electromagnetism; we believe that such a machine may be kept at work without any considerable tax upon the time of the person using it; and we further believe that the only thing which can prevent its coming into use is, the cost of the materials employed in operating it; the statements which we have heard on this point are extremely contradictory and upon the whole are far from encouraging; the time, however, is not remote when this point will be determined.[92]

At this time Davenport was getting plenty of publicity, but no more than token financial support. M. H. Jacobi on the other hand, was faring very differently. Casting round Europe for a sponsor, in May 1837 he petitioned the Czar of Russia for a well-supplied workshop and 8,000 roubles, so that he could 'cover the Neva rather than the Thames or the Tiber with magnetic boats.' Nicholas I, the 'Iron Czar' appreciated the strategic possibility of getting one up on both the British and the Austro-Hungarian navies and rewarded Jacobi with a large grant, stipulating that the experiments should be on the largest scale under the direction of an Imperial Commission, with the special object of investigating whether this moving power could be applied to propelling vessels instead of the steam engine.[93]

In Scotland electromagnetism was seen as an alternative to steam locomotion on the railways. David Mackie, lecturer at the Glasgow Mechanics Institute, John Leadbetter – the President of the Institute – and others offered a prize during the 1838–9 session of six guineas to any student for the best-constructed locomotive engine to be impelled by power derived from electromagnetism. Much to Mackie's disappointment, nobody claimed the prize. Mackie wrote to Leadbetter saying that he thought that this might be:

owing to the notion that there is much more difficulty

in the undertaking than there really is, or to the premium not being sufficient, or to the time allowed for inventing and executing a new machine being rather limited.[94]

For the 1839–40 session, Mackie increased the prize to ten guineas and offered to give every help to the competitors, who were to complete their work by March 1840. He confided to Leadbetter:

> If the Mechanics and Engineers of this country do not bestir themselves, others will; and I shall not be surprised to see Brother Jonathan across at us with an electro-magnetic boat before the next distribution of prizes at the Institution. [95]

Once again, there were no claimants for the prize, but his fears about the plans of Brother Jonathan did not materialise either. For Davenport, with his grandiose plans to cross the Atlantic, ran into financial trouble and it was the well-funded Jacobi who was the first to propel an electric boat on the waters of the River Neva. Omitting any mention of the discomfort that must have been produced by the fumes of nitric and sulphuric acid given off by the batteries, he describes his experiments in a letter to Michael Faraday:

> St Petersburg, June 21, 1839… During the past autumn, and at a season already too advanced, I made, as you may perhaps have learned by the gazattes, the first experiments in navigation on the Neva, with a ten-oared shallop furnished with paddle-wheels, which

were put in motion by an electromagnetic machine. Although we journeyed during entire days and usually with 10 or 12 persons on board, I was not well satisfied with this first trial for there were so many faults of construction and want of insulation in the machines and batteries which could not be repaired on the spot that I was terribly annoyed. All these repairs and important changes being accomplished the experiments will shortly be recommenced... If heaven preserves my health, which is a little affected by continual labours, I hope that within a year of this time, I shall have equipped an electromagnetic vessel of from 40 to 50 horsepower.[96]

Faraday was not usually one to enthuse about the practical applications of electricity, but even he was carried away by Jacobi's news. He wrote back:

To think only of putting an electro magnetic machine into the Great Western or the British Queen & sending them across the Atlantic by it or even to the East Indies! What a glorious thing it would be.[97]

Faraday had Jacobi's letter translated from German and sent it to David Brewster, the Scottish physicist, editor of the Philosophical Magazine, who published it in the September 1839 issue. It was the publication of this letter that spurred the Rev. Professor Patrick Forbes of Aberdeen to write to Faraday bringing Robert Davidson, a fellow townsman, to his attention. Davidson, to borrow the words of David Mackie quoted earlier, had indeed 'bestirred himself' and had some results to show for two years of patient quiet labour.[98] And so it was that Davidson emerged briefly from obscurity, to make his own distinct contribution to the development of electromagnetism.

By 1839, two years into Queen Victoria's reign, the strategic possibilities of electromagnetism as a motive power were beginning to be dimly appreciated. Each nation, or so it seems, saw the practical development of electromagnetic power from a different viewpoint: in America, electromagnetism would be the servant of the housewife and find its place in the factory; in Russia it would be the means of revolutionising the Russian Navy and making the best strategic use of her rivers; in Great Britain, it would be the means of replacing the steam-powered railway locomotive and of rendering boiler explosions a thing of the past. Only in Russia was any financial support forthcoming from the Government: elsewhere inventors had to fend for themselves.

Chapter Four

A Letter to Michael Faraday

IT IS VERY UNLIKELY THAT ROBERT DAVIDSON WOULD HAVE come to the notice of the public or ventured far from Aberdeen, had it not been for the friendship and support of the Reverend Professor Patrick Forbes, Professor of Humanity and lecturer in Chemistry at Kings College, Aberdeen. For although Davidson had a lively and inventive mind, and ran a profitable general chemical and engineering business, he was shy and diffident, almost to a fault: He needed someone in the background to advise and encourage him and he found this support in Patrick Forbes.

Although Forbes was a generation older than Davidson, and his three surviving children by his first wife had grown up, he had married again in 1821.[99] So by the late 1830s his house was once again full of young children; eight to be precise! His second wife Mary Glennie was much of an age with Davidson, being the sister of one of his classmates at Marischal College. So it is neither hard to imagine Forbes as being in tune with the younger generation, nor that Davidson would have felt at home in such company.

Forbes, like a number of other Church of Scotland ministers of his day, seems to have had a deep love of science. For him, there was no artificial division between the spiritual and material needs of men. Rather, he would have said that a practical knowledge of science and the useful arts was a channel whereby the Minister might communicate the love of God to his flock. For, as he once wrote:

> If there be any particle of the old dour leven of Puritanism remaining amongst us, we may be allowed… again publicly to declare that it is not merely the privilege but the duty of clergymen to study nature and cultivate science; for nature was never made by the devil, nor did scientific truth ever come forth from the Father of Lies; and most surely do we know that the calm, clear spirit of philosophical research is much more justly entitled to claim brotherhood with Christ's gospel of mildness and love, than is the bitter and battling spirit so apt to be engendered in the minds of those members of the clerical profession with whom party politics and party pamphleteering swallow up the few hours – and often more than the few – that can be conscientiously spared from the necessary diary of unobtrusive parochial duty.[100]

Forbes graduated from Marischal College in 1793 and in 1797 he accompanied the Duke of Fife to London, where he took the opportunity to continue his studies in chemistry. He was called to the charge of Boharm in 1800, where he soon put his scientific knowledge to use. He was appointed district vaccinator at a time when the new preventive against smallpox was first being tried out. The area in his charge was a large one and, from time to time, the people of Glenlivet and Speyside would descend upon the village in their covered carts and camp near the dispensary that Forbes built on to the Manse. In 1817 he was appointed to the chair of Humanity – Latin – at King's College, to which he added the duties of lecturer in Chemistry and also minister of the second charge at St Machar's Cathedral.[101]

His obituary says that 'he possessed an active mind and a strong constitution and continued to discharge his multifarious duties for many years with untiring zeal and perseverance.'[102] This is an understatement, for he rose at five and rarely went to bed before midnight. As Professor of Humanity, he acquired the nickname of 'Old Prosody', because of his attention to versification and his love of Horace. He was described as a 'keen, clever, irascible, but devoted teacher'.[103]

As a preacher and minister, he was held in sufficient regard to be elected Moderator of the Church of Scotland in 1829. He was active in its affairs for many years and never neglected his pastoral duties.

Chemistry, however, was his real love, and is was to chemistry that he devoted those energies that remained to him when he had fulfilled his other duties. His class at King's was attended by some of the medical students and by arts and divinity students. Extramural students could also attend, and the class was popular with those interested in linen, wool and cotton manufacture. Nor was the class always made up of boisterous students in gowns and apprentices from the town: one of his young daughters was a regular attender for one session, demonstrating what a free-spirited individual he must have been.

Although the knowledge that Forbes imparted was rather elementary, he is said to have fired his students with enthusiasm above the commonplace and to have sown in their minds the idea that amazing discoveries in chemistry and electricity might be made during their lifetimes. He expounded Dalton's Atomic Theory and told his students that before long men would use steam power to travel by land and sea, an idea which caused great merriment among his audience at the time. On one occasion he circled his classroom with a mile of wire in to demonstrate the possibilities of the electric telegraph. 'Gentlemen,' he said, 'in thirty years it will put a girdle around the world and words will flash from land to land in twenty minutes.' This was greeted with profound disbelief by his audience. One farmer's son spoke up for all: 'Na, na. I'll tak a lot from you doctor, but I winna tak that.'[104] So much for the idea that the young are always more progressive than their elders. Forbes died in 1847, having seen some of his more speculative ideas become reality. He was, as one of his contemporaries described him, a grand old professor who went 'before the times'. Davidson was fortunate to have him as a friend and mentor.

Forbes seems to have been aware of Davidson's work from the outset and took an active interest in its progress: it was their custom to meet after the Sunday service and go for a long walk together.[105] We may imagine them, week after week, sharing ideas and dreaming about the future. Forbes would have seen Davidson's progress on batteries; his experiments to determine the best kind of iron and methods of working it to make good electromagnets; the step-by-step improvements in his motors. Then came the day towards the end of September 1839, when

Davidson really had something to show for his efforts. When Forbes took Professor John Fleming to see Davidson they were shown a lathe and a small carriage that could carry two people over the coarse wooden floor of a room: both machines were electrically driven. Forbes wrote in his letter to Faraday:[106]

> The first two machines seen in operation by Dr Fleming and myself, are exceedingly simple, without indeed the least complexity and therefore easily manageable, and not liable to derangement. They also take up very little room... from what can be judged by what is already done, it seems to be probable that a very great power, in no degree even inferior to that of steam, but much more manageable, much less expensive, and occupying greatly less space, if coals be taken into account, may be obtained.

Forbes had read of Jacobi's experiments on the River Neva in the September issue of the Philosophical Magazine and he wasted no time in writing a long letter to Michael Faraday – part of which is quoted above – to tell him of Davidson's labours in the same field of discovery. The letter was carefully written, with the hope and intention that Faraday would pass it on to the editor of the Philosophical Magazine for publication.

Why, you might ask, did Forbes not write to the editor directly? Perhaps Forbes thought that a letter forwarded by Faraday, whose name was much better known than his, would not only be more likely to be published, but would register all the more clearly in the mind of the reader. It was part of a plan to enable Davidson to stake his claim for recognition, without the need to go through the time-consuming and expensive process of taking out a patent. We will come back to this point shortly, merely noting for the present the drift of Forbes' thought in the last paragraph of the letter:

> In short the inventions of Mr Davidson seem to be so interesting to railroad proprietors in particular, that it would be very much for their interest to take up the subject, and be at the expense of making the experiments necessary to bring this power into operation on the grand scale, which would indeed be very trifling to a company, while it is very serious for an individual by no means rich, and who has already expended so much of his time and money from the mere desire of perfecting machines which he expected would be so beneficial to his country and to mankind. For it deserves to be mentioned that he has made no secret of his operations, but has shown and explained all that he has done to everyone who wished it. His motives have been quite disinterested, and I shall deem it a reproach to our country and our countrymen if he is allowed to languish in obscurity, and not have an opportunity afforded to him of perfecting his inventions and bringing them into operation, when they promise to be productive of such incalculable advantages.

Forbes' letter to Faraday was widely reprinted, but it did not lead to any further correspondence. This may have been because neither the construction details nor the principles of operation of Davidson's machines were given. Seven months went by, and then on 9 July 1840 the Mechanic's Magazine published a description of a patent granted one week before to William Taylor of the United States of America. This motor was exhibited at the Colliseum in London and was even briefly mentioned in the Times.[107]

Here was a case of parallel invention: Taylor's motor operated in the same way as Davidson's – both being what we would now call 'switched field' reluctance motors.[108] Even the motor constructions were very similar, with a series of transverse iron bars mounted on the rotor drum and stationary electromagnets mounted on a solid frame. Nor could you say for certain which of the two men began his work first, for Davidson appears to started in 1837 and Taylor took out his original US patent in 1838. Neither of the two men could have known that their motors were somewhat similar to those already built by Nicholas Callan in Ireland.

Davidson had not taken out a patent, quite deliberately, it appears. However, Taylor's patent was a potential threat to his own freedom of action and he responded to its publication by writing a vigorous, but fair, letter to the Mechanic's Magazine to defend himself.[109]

I am aware that in coming forward as I now do to contest the right of an individual to the exclusive possession of an invention for which he has obtained a patent, I place myself in a somewhat suspicious position and however well satisfied I might be of the justice of my claim, were it not that the evidence I shall be able to offer in support of it, is such as I think cannot be withstood, I should willingly shun the risk of incurring the imputation, which attempts such as that which I now make not infrequently deserve. As matters stand

I cannot see but that I am perfectly justified in seeking to vindicate my claim.

He then argues his case thus:

Now I conceive that if I can show that the application to which Mr Taylor, in his specification, lays exclusive claim, was known to, and practised by me years before Mr Taylor's Patent was heard of, I shall have established my claim to originality at least, if not priority of invention. And if I am further able to show that I have made no secret of my operation, but have all along willingly exhibited and explained all that I have accomplished to everyone that wished it, I know enough of the patent laws to be aware that neither Mr Taylor, nor anyone else, though fortified by fifty patents, can stop me from following out my researches, and applying their results to any purpose I choose.

The principle of 'magnetic action' mentioned in Taylor's patent – the subject of the dispute – is described in Forbes' original letter to Faraday as employing 'the electromagnetic power in producing motion by simply suspending the magnetism without a change of poles'. This means that the electromagnets that were used to act on the iron bars on the rotor were merely switched on and off in sequence, at the right time, to produce torque and that at no time was the current in the electromagnets reversed. There was no need to reverse the current, as there would have been if permanent or electromagnets had been substituted for the iron bars. It was a simple motor with simple switching and it is this that makes the reluctance motor attractive – in principle at least – in these days of electronic switching. The reluctance principle itself was not novel. One can only suppose that – because of the rudimentary understanding of electromagnetism at that time – the distinction between the reluctance principle itself and its various practical embodiments was not clear. It is hardly surprising, therefore, that an inventor might think that he was exploiting a new principle – as Taylor and Davidson both appear to have thought – and not realise that he was exploiting a variation of one already established.

Having compared the wording of Taylor's patent with that of Forbes' letter, using the latter as if it were a comparable motor specification, Davidson went on:

> Now I appeal with utmost confidence, to any men possessing even the most superficial knowledge of electromagnetism whether there is the slightest difference between my invention, 'accomplished' as Dr. Forbes declares, 'about two years previous to the 7th October 1839' and that to which Mr Taylor lays claim in his specification, dated May 2nd 1840. They are so clearly one and the same invention that I apprehend nothing further need be said to establish their identity.[110]

After dealing with the subject matter of the patent and dates of disclosure, Davidson listed the prominent citizens of Aberdeen who 'saw and examined my machine long before either Mr Taylor or his patent were heard of'. Among them was the aged Dr Forsyth, inventor of the percussion lock, who was Minister of Belhevie and a close friend of Patrick Forbes, whose own experiences of treatment as an inventor had been far from happy.

Having thus established the positions with which I set out, namely, the originality, and so far as appears the priority of my invention, and also the fact of its publication by me previous to the granting of Mr Taylor's patent, I repeat the determination I have announced, namely, that I shall continue my researches, and apply their results to any purpose I choose, just as if no such person or patent were in existence.

I have no quarrel with Mr Taylor, nor do I bear him any ill will; on the contrary, I hail with satisfaction the appearance of so efficient a fellow labourer as Mr Taylor has proved himself in a favourite field of Science. Nevertheless I cannot consent to be deprived of the use of an invention I have made, and which without fee or reward, I have freely communicated for the public benefit. And therefore I take this public manner of intimating to Mr Taylor the course I intend to pursue in reference to my invention.

The editor of the Mechanic's Magazine added a footnote to the letter, in which he concluded that Taylor's patent would still be valid in law 'as long as nobody before the patentee had advanced the length of making it publicly known and used in England'. Patent law, so it seems, had not advanced sufficiently by that date for a disclosure by Davidson in Scotland to count as a disclosure for the United Kingdom as a whole. So Taylor's patent would stand, in England at least.

The editor, it seems, was used to receiving letters from angry inventors, for, having come down on the side of Taylor, he then qualified his remarks with a comment about Davidson:

> Having volunteered so much on the one side of the
> question, we may be forgiven for adding that whatever
> may be the historic or legal rights of Mr Davidson, no
> one can fail to admire the candid, temperate and truthful
> spirit in which they are asserted.

There are two interesting aspects of Davidson's letter to the
Mechanic's Magazine. These are: firstly, as we have seen above,
the way in which Davidson uses Forbes' letter to Faraday to
defend himself and to act as a kind of substitute for a patent
(he would extensively reprint Forbes' letter on handbills for
this purpose later); secondly, the light that it throws on his
personality.

His letter reflects both a ferocious determination not to be
thwarted by any anticipated restrictive move by Taylor and a
balanced attitude to the inventor himself and his capability for
original thinking.

Davidson calls Taylor an efficient fellow labourer and hails his
appearance on the scene with satisfaction, but, significantly, he
makes it clear that he regards Taylor and himself to be independent
inventors.

> I say independent inventors, for I should be sorry if
> it were thought that I meant to insinuate what I do
> not myself believe, that Mr Taylor borrowed either
> his principle from me, or the idea of his machine from
> mine.

The letter shows that Davidson was able to draw comparisons
between his own machines and those of a rival in a rational
manner. His conclusion that: 'a more extraordinary resemblance

– extending even to the minutest details – never existed between the ideas of two independent inventors' shows that he was able to avoid the kind of emotional entanglement to which some inventors are prone and that he was able to dispute facts without calling the integrity of a rival into question. No doubt he had been helped to see things in this light by Forbes himself. In the event, Taylor never answered Davidson's letter and no more was heard of him.

Davidson's letter to the Mechanic's Magazine shows that he had a reasonable grasp of patent law: I therefore conclude that he deliberately chose not to patent his motors. There are three possible factors that might have contributed to this decision: philosophical, pragmatic and financial.

Firstly, from a philosophical viewpoint, Davidson seems to have thought that knowledge should be passed on for the benefit of society in general, as we learn from his advertisement of October 1840:

> Mr Davidson has declined securing to himself by patent the exclusive right to the use of this new power, being willing that all to whom the possession of a cheap simple and safe substitute for steam power is an object should freely avail themselves of the advantage to be drawn from his invention.

The main object of his exhibitions was to enable others to become 'acquainted with the capabilities of the electromagnetic power'. The entrance fee was to cover his expenses, rather than a means of making a fortune. This attitude differs from that of some of his contemporaries, who regarded a patent as a gateway to fame and fortune. Davidson may have been influenced by

Forbes. Alternatively, he may have felt that if electromagnetic machines became widely used, there would be a large increase in demand for the kind of chemicals that he would be in a strong position to supply.

Secondly, from a pragmatic viewpoint, in those days patents were very hard to come by, because of the complicated procedures involved. If an inventor wished to survey the prior art before taking steps to patent their own idea, then a written copy of the specification of almost any patent, according to Highton, would have cost between £10 and £40. Highton continues:[111]

> Hundreds of patents are taken out annually, yet a man living anywhere out of London, unless he comes up to town and searches in the enrollment offices of the Courts of Chancery – a process which might detain him many days at large expense – cannot know what he is forbidden by law either to make, use or sell.

> Again no classified index is kept at the Enrollment Office so that unless a person employs a patent agent or some good fortune attend him, he may search for days and weeks in a variety of books and rolls of parchment without knowing whether he is or is not forbidden to make any article which he has just invented, but which may for ought he can learn to the contrary, have been, during the previous fourteen years patented by someone else.

> Until a proper index is made for all patents and published periodically and sold at rates similar to Acts of Parliament and until all specifications are printed also

and sold at similar prices – such a confused and difficult state of things must, it is feared, continue to remain, to the utter shame and disgrace of this inventive and mechanical nation.[112]

In those days, the specifications were written, often illegibly, on parchment and the accompanying plans were often stitched in many yards from the specifications to which they referred. Nor did the Patent Office make the searchers task easy, for, as Highton continues:

Not a word may be copied at the time of reading of the specification in the Office – nor will the officials copy for payment a portion only of the specification, and of every simple sentence in perhaps 16 or 18 skins of parchment and that too of perhaps 20 to 30 specifications before he can be confident that the erection of the telegraph he desires will not bring down upon him some half a dozen actions in law from various quarters: such are the glorious uncertainties of the matter... The author having gone through all the nuisance of this searching and reading of the specifications of every patent for electric telegraphs and having endured the horrible torture of learning claims by heart, and of filling his head to the full in the Enrollment Office and emptying it on paper immediately he has emerged from the door of those dreaded precincts, can well bear witness to the abominable and disgraceful state of things as regards the present state of the patent laws in this kingdom.

The third impediment to taking out a patent was the cost. Charles Dickens vividly describes the process in *A poor man's tale of a patent.* This involved obtaining the Queen's signature twice and feeing the following dignitaries: the Home Secretary; the Lord Chancellor; the Privy Seal; the Clerk of the Patents; the Lord Chancellor's Purse-Bearer; the Clerk of the Hanaper; the Deputy Clerk of the Hanaper; the Deputy Sealer; and the Deputy Chaff-wax.

> No man in England could get a patent for an india-rubber band, or an iron hoop without feeing all of them. Some of them over and over again. I went through thirty-five stages. I began with the Queen upon the Throne. I ended with the Deputy Chaff-wax. Note. I should like to see the Deputy Chaff-wax. Is it a man or what is it?[113]

The cost of this rigmarole was about £100 for England, but for the United Kingdom as a whole it came to about £300. It seems reasonable to suppose that Davidson would have viewed the prospect of a long and expensive patent application as merely an impediment to his experimental programme. With limited resources, his best protection probably was indeed Forbes' letter of commendation to Faraday.

Davidson's reasons for not taking out a patent seem entirely sound and to judge him by later standards – when patents were cheap and the law better formulated – underestimates the care with which he and Forbes went into the matter. Forbes letter was, in the circumstances, the best and cheapest guarantee of his freedom to experiment that could have been devised at the time.

Why, we might ask, had Davidson not made his work known

outside Aberdeen? Here he was, in the summer of 1840, nearly a year after the publication of Forbes' letter, unknown and without sponsors. Part of the answer must lie in his shyness and diffidence and part in a wish to perfect his ideas before launching them upon the public. Perhaps too he thought there was no particular need to hurry. If so, Taylor's patent must have come as a rude shock. Some of his friends, among them William Knight, had tried to persuade him to go to London to seek sponsors in 1837,[114] but had not managed to get him to go. So we may speculate that it was the impact of the publication of Taylor's patent, coupled with prompting from his friends, that persuaded Davidson – at long last – to open an exhibition of electromagnetism. We may imagine Forbes, in his pastoral capacity, taking him to task for burying his talents and telling him that it was wrong for any Christian man to keep to himself knowledge of the mysteries of the Universe – knowledge which might yet benefit mankind. William Knight, on the other hand, would have given him a taste of his rough tongue. However, even now, in spite of the advice of his friends, Davidson seems to have thought that he could obtain sponsorship locally: he opened his exhibition neither in London, nor Edinburgh, but in Aberdeen.

∽

One interesting sidelight on this period in Davidson's life (1839–40) is that he is recorded as being one of the twelve original members of the Aberdeen Philosophical Society – 'constituted of the cultivators of Science in and around Aberdeen'.[115] He was the only member who was neither a university Professor nor lecturer, indicating that for a short period he was held in high esteem by the small scientific community in Aberdeen. The preliminary meeting was held at the house of William Gregory, Professor of Medicine and Chemistry at King's College, with Professor Fleming in the chair. Subsequent meetings were held in the more convivial surroundings of the Lemon Tree Tavern. The other members were men of standing and seven find a place in the *Dictionary of National Biography*. Five of them came to Aberdeen in 1839, as a result of the reorganisation of the combined Medical School into two separate schools at King's and Marischal Colleges. Four of the original members had left Aberdeen by 1845, including Professor Fleming, who left as a direct result of the Disruption of the Church of Scotland in 1843. So, when Davidson returned to Aberdeen after his prolonged absence in Edinburgh and London, he would have found the society much changed and with a new set of moving spirits running it. This change can be seen from the lecture programmes, which shift their emphasis – initially on chemistry and geology – to other more general subjects as time goes on. From the eighth session (1846–7) onwards, the scientific papers become fewer and appear alongside those on the theology of the Greeks, etc. The Society membership had changed, as had their interests. It is not therefore altogether surprising that Davidson does not seem to have kept up his membership.

Chapter Five

Exhibitions in Aberdeen and Edinburgh

THE ABERDEEN MECHANIC'S INSTITUTE HAD BEEN FOUNDED IN 1824 but failed to live up to the high hopes of its founders: within a few years it was moribund. However, by 1840 public interest had revived and that autumn the Institute Committee decided to hold an exhibition, with the purpose of raising sufficient funds to build a new hall:[116] exhibits and donations were solicited from the citizens of Aberdeen and from other Mechanic's Institutes. The exhibition was a great success and raised a lot of money. Robert Davidson exhibited a few items at the main exhibition, such as an air gun and an electrical machine, but he also held an exhibition of his own in a separate building in Union Street. Whether this was because of a lack of space in the main exhibition, or because Davidson was seeking for some kind of identity of his own, we do not know. Davidson advised the public of his forthcoming exhibition in these words:

ELECTROMAGNETIC EXHIBITION

MR ROBERT DAVIDSON begs to intimate that he has, for the last three years been engaged in a course of experiments on ELECTRO-MAGNETISM, with a view to devising means for the employment of the Magnetic Influence as a moving power. In this object he flatters himself he has succeeded: and he trusts the time is not far distant when, on account of its greater cheapness and simplicity, and its perfect freedom from danger, the ELECTROMAGNETIC POWER shall have superseded steam for many, or most of the purposes to which the latter power is now applied. Mr Davidson has declined securing to himself by patent the exclusive right to the use of this new power, being willing that all to whom the possession of a cheap, simple, and safe substitute for steam power is an object, should freely avail themselves of the advantages to be drawn from his invention. For this purpose – to afford to all an opportunity of becoming acquainted with the capabilities of the Electro Magnetic Power – Mr Davidson intends opening an Exhibition, the principal features of which he will here briefly detail.

The Exhibition will consist of the following pieces of apparatus actuated by the Electro Magnetic Power:

1. A MODEL OF A LOCOMOTIVE CARRIAGE
This model is of a size sufficient to carry two persons; and it will be shown in operation on a railway.

2. A TURNING LATHE

The lathe is furnished with appropriate tools, so that any person acquainted with the art of turning may have an opportunity of proving the efficiency of the driving power.

3. A SMALL PRINTING MACHINE

The arrangements of the magnets in Nos. 2 and 3 present different modifications of the same principle; while that of the magnets in No. 1 is upon an entirely different principle.

4. AN ELECTRO-MAGNET

This is intended to exhibit the intensity of the Magnetic attraction. When supplied with a suitable battery, it will suspend a weight of several tons.

5. A MACHINE FOR COMMUNICATING THE ELECTRIC SHOCK

The combustion of Metals by Electromagnetism, and other phenomena will also be shown. The Exhibition will commence on Tuesday next, the 6th October in the Hall, No 36, Union Street. The Hall will be open from 1 till 2 afternoon and from 7 till 8 evening.

ADMITTANCE – ONE SHILLING

Aberdeen, 36 Union Street, October 2, 1840[117]

The exhibition ran for about three weeks concurrently with the exhibition at The Mechanic's Institution. The attendance figures for the main exhibition may therefore give some idea of the numbers who might have seen Davidson's machines. The Aberdeen Journal of October 14 records that on the previous Thursday '1100 visitors had the satisfaction of witnessing the collection'.[118]

On 23 October, the same paper went on to write of Davidson's exhibition:

> Our ingenious townsman's Electromagnetic inventions continue to attract many visitors. Last week they were inspected by Dr Hamel from Russia, a gentleman well known in the scientific world, who expressed his high gratification with the exhibition.[119]

Officially the visitor from Russia – known to the world because of his involvement in the first climbing accident on Mont Blanc in 1820[120] – having first attended the Autumn Meeting of the British Association in Glasgow had then gone on to a fossil hunting expedition in the Highlands.[121] What the Aberdeen Journal did not know was that Joseph Hamel – a Volga German and a member of the Russian Imperial Academy of Sciences – was employed specifically by the Russian government to gather information relative to the progress of science and arts in Great Britain.[122] So it seems highly probable that a detailed report of Davidson's exhibition found its way back to St Petersburg where, for all we know, it may lie in some dusty archive to this day.

There is something oddly fascinating and slightly mysterious in the notion of the former tutor and travelling companion to the then Tsar of Russia just dropping in to visit an exhibition of electromagnetism in Aberdeen. The city may have been merely a convenient stopping point on his grand tour, in which case he would have come across the exhibition more or less by chance. On the other hand, he may have come to Aberdeen quite deliberately to find out more about Davidson. Arguably the latter is the most likely. After all, the Tsar had spent quite substantial sums of money on funding Jacobi's electromagnetic boat and it seems entirely reasonable that he would be keen to know the likely degree of competition from elsewhere.

The Aberdeen Constitutional, 6 November 1840, says:

> Electro-Magnetism – Mr Davidson's invaluable invention is now set down by common consent as the desideratum that has been wanting to perfect the power of locomotive agency. Several thousands have visited the exhibition, among whom was Professor Hamel whose opinion was decidedly favourable to the principle. At a meeting of the British Association in Glasgow the other week, Professor Jacobi read a paper on the power of electro-magnetism, which seemed to point to some great improvement in the science, but the principle of Mr Davidson's machine is altogether different from that on which Jacobi's experiments were made. Professor Jacobi produces motion by changing the poles of the magnets; Mr Davidson by cutting off the galvanic current at given points – the power alternating as the rotation proceeds from a neutralised magnet to a newly changing one. We would earnestly press the consideration of Mr Davidson's invention on the patronage of those who have both the means and the inclination to encourage genius. Were a company formed to carry out the principles, we have not the

slightest doubt, but in a very few years there would not be a locomotive used without a magnetic propeller; and considering the number of accidents that are daily occurring on railways, it is especially to be desired that it should supersede the steam engine.

The Aberdeen Banner was equally favourable in its comments about Davidson's exhibition. It 'enjoyed a rich treat in visiting the Exhibition of our talented townsman' and it went on to describe him as 'this second Watt'. It got a little carried away on the subject of the acid waste and the scrap electrodes from the batteries, which, it claimed, yielded 'a product which in the market will bring at the hour three times the cost of the materials'.[123] If this had been true, then Davidson would have been well on his way to making a fortune.

When the exhibition closed in late October, Davidson began to turn his attention towards the possibility of constructing a railway locomotive for use on the Edinburgh and Glasgow Railway, then under construction.

In early May 1841 Davidson set out for Edinburgh, taking with him letters of recommendation to well-known citizens who might help him. He must have aroused some interest be-cause on 17 July 1841 the Edinburgh Weekly Chronicle called upon the Ladies and Gentlemen of Edinburgh 'to extend their patronage as encouraging a genius of very high order'. His most useful introduction was to Robert Chambers, the publisher.[124] Chambers was a man who responded positively to new ideas and took the trouble to visit the exhibition. Feeling that his readers ought to be interested in a new motive power, he wrote in the Edinburgh Journal:[125]

from what fell under our observation, we incline to believe that here at last has been manifested that great desideratum – something to supersede steam power. As yet the discovery is in its infancy, but by skilful improvement and enterprise, it cannot fail soon to rise into importance.

Chambers was sufficiently impressed by what he had seen to offer:

to allow Mr Davidson to fit up an apparatus for turning our printing machinery, which however from other arrangements he was obliged to decline.

Had Davidson taken up Chambers' offer and successfully powered even a small printing press electrically, what was printed would have found its way into Chambers' Edinburgh Journal and his 'Information for the People', both of which had a wide circulation beyond the borders of Scotland. Davidson had missed the one really good opportunity that he ever had to bring himself to the attention of the public: he never had another one.

Notices of Davidson's exhibition appeared in the press and were duly copied, as the custom then was. In September 1841, the Civil Engineers and Architects Journal copied a notice of the exhibition that had recently appeared in The Scotsman. It concluded:

Mr Davidson's discovery, has received the approbation of numerous scientific gentlemen, who consider that Mr Davidson has succeeded in showing the perfect applicability of magnetism as a motive power to engines of every description. It would no doubt be desirable, however, to see experiments tried out on a larger scale; which Mr Davidson we understand is anxious to do, but is deterred by want of funds.[126]

Davidson, if he had read that issue of the Civil Engineers and Architects Journal, might have been perturbed to find below the notice of his exhibition another entitled: 'Travelling by Electro-magnetic Power'.

We are informed that a distance of 57 miles has been travelled on the common road, in a Bath chair, by electromagnetic power in one hour and a half; and further that the applier comes over daily from St Albans to the Bank of England in the said chair in half an hour at an expense of sixpence.

Davidson must have thought that he now had some stiff competition. However, the next issue quoting the Times would have set his mind at rest:

Hoax by Bank Clerk – last month we transferred into our columns an extract from the Literary Gazette giving a short account of a newly-discovered method of propulsion, whereby a common garden or invalid chair could be propelled along a common road by a galvanic power at the rate of 40 miles an hour; and it was further stated that the young man who had dis-covered this new power daily travelled from St Albans to the Bank of England in half an hour – a distance of 22 miles! Great curiosity was naturally excited by the supposed discovery and the young man, who is a bank clerk, was questioned concerning it both by the governor of the Bank, and also by Mr Smee, the cashier,[127] etc. He was invited by the latter, and by several other persons, to display the powers of his new machine, but made repeated excuses for the delay; He first excused himself on the score of illness, and on being again pressed to exhibit the machine, he stated that he had driven it accidentally against a post and shattered it to pieces. Upon being, however, more closely questioned, he at last confessed that the whole story was a hoax and that no such machine had ever existed, save in the fertile imagination of the supposed inventor. This denouement was only made known on Thursday, and it has created a great sensation in the Bank of England. The motive of the youth for the above hoax cannot be accounted for. We are informed, however, that some such galvanic power does exist but that the expense is too great to allow of its being made use of.

All through the rest of 1841 Davidson continued to exhibit, devoting part of his time to interesting the Royal Scottish Society of Arts (RSSA) in his work and part to getting the Edinburgh and Glasgow Railway Company to give him some support.

In November 1841 the Committee of the RSSA voted on a motion by the Secretary that:

the sum of £15 be given out of the experimental fund in aid of any subscriptions which may be raised towards enabling Mr Davidson of Aberdeen to construct an Engine of any kind on the large scale to be propelled by electro magnetism for the purpose of discovering the relation which may exist between *size* and *power*. The money to be expended at the sight of a committee; but Mr Davidson to be left uncontrolled as to the method to be followed in his experiments.

A committee of three – Mr Glover, Mr Crawford and Dr Fyfe – was appointed, with Mr Glover as convener, to

superintend the experiment and to report whether it fulfils the condition for which the sum has been voted and, when the experiment is concluded, to report the result. The money to be paid as soon as the committee shall have reported that in their opinion the said Conditions have been fulfilled.

In the event, the money was not paid out until 1843 and we must assume that Davidson shouldered the financial burden for the locomotive himself. There is no evidence that anyone else besides the RSSA funded him in any way at all.[128]

Davidson kept his exhibition open into the early months of 1842. John Clerk Maxwell, a member of the RSSA, recorded in his diary that on Saturday 12 February 1842 he took his ten-year-old son James to see the electromagnetic machines.[129] Presumably the exhibition made an impression on both father and son. Could it have been this visit to Davidson's exhibition that set Maxwell along the path that was to lead him later to explore electromagnetism and to formulate the unified theory of electromagnetism? Unfortunately, John Maxwell's diary has been lost and there now no way of knowing whether he recorded more than the bare detail quoted by Garnett in his biography.

Chapter Six

1842 Trials on the Edinburgh & Glasgow Railway

With a digression on the subject of the
'Anti-Sunday-Travelling Saints'

THE EDINBURGH AND GLASGOW RAILWAY COMPANY (THE
Railway) was incorporated by Act of Parliament in 1838 and the
railway link between the two cities was completed early in 1842.
From the start, the Railway carried large numbers of passengers,
although the conditions of travel left much to be desired. One of
the Railway's well-wishers wrote to the Railway Times:

> It is universally said by all who have tried both, that the
> second-class carriages are colder than the third, owing
> to the draught of air to which the former are exposed,
> while in the latter you are merely in the open air, with
> the wind generally either in your face or at your back.
> I came from Falkirk to Edinburgh in a second-class
> carriage in July, having been fourteen days from home,
> travelling by land and water, and never had occasion

to use my greatcoat until I entered this carriage; and if cold was at all felt in July; how will it be possible to endure it in the winter months? ... Why not also provide seats for the third-class passengers? Surely they also are entitled to be treated like human beings, not like cattle in a pen.[130]

Other writers complained bitterly about the soot and smoke that came the way of the passengers, so perhaps it is not surprising that an electromagnetic locomotive would have seemed an attractive alternative to steam, at least in theory. But it was not technical problems or soot and smoke that bedevilled the Railway, but quarrels between the local Committees in Glasgow and Edinburgh and a long, acrimonious argument about Sunday travelling.

Local Committees in Edinburgh and Glasgow had been set up in the two cities in order to raise capital to build the railway, and initially each committee was responsible for running its own end of the line. This arrangement worked reasonably well until the line – the construction of which had been begun at its extremities – was almost complete. At this stage, each Local Committee tried to impose its will on the other, and run the whole line. During 1841, the legal battle got out of hand and consumed much of the Director's energies. The dispute was only resolved by making both Local Committees subservient to a reconstituted Main Board, under the chairmanship of John Leadbetter. The Directors were reduced in number from twenty-four to fifteen – six from Glasgow, four from Edinburgh and the remaining five from the shareholders at large. Up until then, there had been two local secretaries – one in Edinburgh and the other in Glasgow – but in the reorganisation the number was reduced to one and Charles Forbes Davidson, the Edinburgh Secretary and an Edinburgh lawyer, became redundant. This must have put Robert Davidson at a disadvantage, because Charles Davidson – not a relative – was both an Aberdonian and a fellow alumnus of Marischal College.

The Glasgow and Edinburgh factions might fight for management control, but in the end common sense prevailed, because double management of a single railway was a manifest absurdity. The squabble over Sunday travelling was a different matter. It split the Board, it split the shareholders and it spilled over into a very public controversy that the public entered into with gusto through correspondence in the newspapers. When the line opened, two trains were scheduled to run in each direction on Sundays. This was anathema to the Sabbatarian 'Anti-Sunday-Travelling Saints',[131] who fought hard to get the trains abolished. The Directors had a dilemma: the Chairman, and a few, mindful of local opinion, were against Sunday travelling. Others, representing the shareholders at large, wanted the best possible return on investment and were therefore in favour of Sunday travelling. There was, however, a vocal minority of shareholders prepared to go to considerable and sometimes devious lengths to get the Sunday trains abolished: by buying up shares and splitting them and in some cases obtaining false signatures on petitions.[132]

At first sight, the argument might seem a simple one: was it right to provide transport for the travelling public on Sundays, or not? Many sincere objectors felt it their duty to defend their concept of the Sabbath, but there were others whose motives were suspect. Objectors claimed that Sunday travelling by train was setting a new precedent, but this was not the case. Two Sunday mail coaches plied the route between Edinburgh and Glasgow each way, and – as one shareholder pointed out in the Railway Times – if mail coaches why not mail trains? No one seemed to be in the least bit worried that the mail coach set off at twelve noon, in the middle of Divine Service. Pleasure steamers sailed the Clyde on Sundays and even the Chairman of the Railway, Mr John Leadbetter had been known to hire a coach and travel round Loch Tay on a Sunday afternoon.[133] Anyone with a vested interest in the Forth-Clyde Canal, Turnpike Roads, mail coaches or pleasure steamers would have wished to restrict Sunday travel on the railway. Others might have a subconscious fear of what might happen, should the working man have the freedom to travel widely on his day of rest.

For months the papers and the Railway Times carried pages of correspondence from both sides which reached the heights of silliness. The Witness [134]circulated, in all seriousness, a peculiar notion that:

> The Scotch Sabbath breaker, especially if he belong to the humbler classes, will be found to be a much worse man than the Sabbath Breaker of the sister kingdom.

The Morning Chronicle – tongue in cheek – expressed the gist of the argument thus:

> Amongst a set of Pagans like the English, the rail road people, bad as they are may not be much worse than other people; but amongst a holy people like the Scotch, a man who breaks the Sabbath will be ready for the commission of any deed, however atrocious, and therefore the least which any person travelling on the Sabbath can expect from being driven by a Scotch engineman is to have his neck broken.[135]

The Morning Chronicle went on to say that it thought the circulation of such Sabbatical Scottish newspapers would make more infidels than all that Voltaire, Hume, Volney or Paine ever wrote.

The Glasgow Argus[136] pointed out that some of the self-styled Edinburgh and Glasgow 'Anti Sabbath Desecrators' were also shareholders in a Sunday Gas Manufactory,

> and that no one had ever been heard to say that the manufacture or use of gas on a Sunday was wrong. Had to objectors to Sunday travel refused to allow gas manufactured on a Sunday to be introduced into their own houses? Nay are not even our own churches brilliantly lighted up by it on the Lord's Evening, and did any of our Doctors in Divinity, or Probationers of the Church, whether Established or Dissenters, turn round the gas cock with indignation, or puff out the lights afforded them by this manufactory on a Sunday – Never. What is the difference, in a moral point of view, between a manufactory of gas and a manufactory of steam... Is the smoke of the gas holder holier on the Sabbath-day than the smoke of the railway carriage? We leave the saints to answer us these questions if they please. But we have them on another very palpable tact. Will our Bains, or our Leadbetters refuse to take the interest on their bonds or bills on the Sabbath day? Do they make any deductions on that account? Will the good Mr John Bain, in particular, who has trafficked in horses and carriages and mailbags on the Sunday, be pleased to inform us whether he gave any deduction to the widow for her rent on a Sunday?

Feelings ran high and even the Reverend Robert Murray M'Cheyne of St Peter's Church Dundee – by repute a man of saintly piety – lapsed briefly into the language of the demagogue, calling the Directors that favoured Sunday travel: 'infidels, scoffers, men of unholy lives, the enemies of all righteousness, moral suicides, sinners against light, traitors to their country, robbers and murderers'.[137]

The issue was formally settled by a special meeting held immediately after the half-yearly meeting in the spring of 1842. Deputations from numerous interested parties were received and a six-hour discussion followed, at the end of which a motion to run two trains each way on Sundays was put to the meeting and carried by a two to one majority. As a result, the Railway continued to run trains on Sunday, to the discomfort of the Chairman John Leadbetter, whose friends had been behind the move to abolish the trains. At the next half-yearly meeting on 23 August 1842, Leadbetter resigned, and was replaced by John Learmouth.

So we see that while Robert Davidson was building his locomotive, the Directors of the Railway had other and much weightier matters on their minds. At the very time when Davidson's locomotive was about to begin its trials, the Chairman – known to be interested in electromagnetic power and therefore quite possibly the most supportive member of the Board – resigned. The resulting changes could explain why the company seems to have lost any interest in the project and treated Davidson so meanly.

Unfortunately the records of the Railway, extensive though they are – do not mention a written contract between Davidson and the company to build a locomotive. It therefore seems likely that any agreement between the parties was very loose and possibly not in writing. William Knight in his manuscript notes[138] provides indirect and independent confirmation of this when he writes: 'The Edinburgh and Glasgow Railway Company engaged him in the following winter (1841) to construct a large engine.' And a little further on he says: 'the slow motion of his engine at Edinburgh he (Davidson) ascribes to the wheels having been made by far too small; – it was left in the Company's hands'. Since the company was prepared to interfere with the project, it seems reasonable to infer some commitment to it on their part.

The likelihood is that the Company agreed to provide Davidson with the use of facilities – perhaps the corner of a carriage shed at Haymarket, limited access to a workshop and assistance with the manufacture of some components for the locomotive – but that Davidson had to provide all the materials for the motors and the batteries himself. The company would probably not have been prepared to construct large wheels to his specification because of the cost of patterns and the making of castings, or perhaps because they felt that they knew more about railway construction than he did. He may have had to be content with two pairs of cast-off carriage wheels and axles for his engine, and this may account for the comments of Knight reported above. Robert Rettie, the inventor and a contemporary of Davidson at Marischal College, says in a letter published under the name of PRO BONO PUBLICO in the Railway Times on 10 January 1843[139] that when he had last seen Davidson three months previously '[h]e had been engaged nearly twelvemonths, and devoting his whole time, with the aid of a young man, an assistant...' This suggests that construction of the locomotive began in the autumn of 1841.

It was first tried out in one of the carriage sheds in the presence of several of the Directors, on 17 September 1842.

The ponderous machine, weighing between five and six tons, was instantly set in motion on the immersion of the metallic plates into the troughs containing a solution of sulphuric acid. One curious phenomenon connected with the motion of this new and ingenious instrument was the extent and brilliancy of the repeated electric flashes which accompanied the action of the machinery.[140]

From this we learn, firstly, that the battery was used as a kind of electrolytic speed controller by lowering the plates into the acid solution and, secondly, that sparking at the commutators was very noticeable, indicating that large quantities of stored magnetic energy were being dissipated at each break in the flow of current.

Fortunately David Mackie – who lectured at the Glasgow Mechanic's Institute and whom we have already come across offering a prize for the best-constructed electromagnetic loco-motive – published an article in the Glasgow Practical Mechan-ics' Magazine in November 1842[141] that shows his representation of the locomotive, which is wildly out of scale and not to be interpreted too literally. The locomotive, called Galvani, was about sixteen feet long by seven feet broad and weighed about six tons. The locomotive was directly driven by motors on each of its two axles and these were of the reluctance type, comprising a set of stationary electromagnets that could be switched on and off with a commutator and rotating iron bars attached to a drum mounted on each axle. The picture shows four electromagnets per axle and three axial bars of iron on each rotor drum, split in the middle. It is clear that each axle motor is built on the same principle as the motor used to drive the small lathe and described in Chapter 5, only with double set of electromagnets. It is possible that the sets of iron bars used for the two halves of each motor were circumferentially displaced from one another, but this is pure conjecture. If they had been displaced, and the timing of the commutation of current to the electromagnets had been similarly displaced, it would have been possible to make the motors more or less self-starting. Otherwise the division of the iron into two half lengths seems somewhat pointless.

Originally two batteries of about twenty cells each were placed at the ends of the carriage. The plates of iron and amalgamated zinc were twelve inches wide by fifteen inches deep. The general design was similar to the battery described in the previous chapter.

The four commutators used to commutate currents in the electromagnets were set on the axles, just outside the wheels, an arrangement about which Mackie comments: 'but we should think that as they are a nice and important part of the apparatus they would be safer within the wheels',

All in all, Mackie's drawing is most confusing – either the author had not seen the machine, or else he was trying to avoid giving away too much – it is impossible to say which.

Davidson had his troubles. Firstly, the battery power was not sufficient and had to be augmented by an additional battery on each side of the locomotive. Secondly, he found that the unbalanced attractive forces between rotor and stator iron – given the lack of rigidity in a wooden frame – were so great that they came into contact. William Henley, presumably getting his information directly from Davidson, reports:

> when first put in action, so powerful was the attractive
> force of the magnets, that the frame-work was not

strong enough to withstand the strain; it was drawn
together, and, consequently, the first experiment failed.
Money not being at hand to construct another carriage,
Mr Davidson was obliged to patch up the old one, and
removed the magnets to such a distance from the iron
to be attracted, that then at their nearest point he could
introduce his hand into the space between them.[142]

How frustrating it must have been to make this unsatisfactory
improvisation and how sad that no one was prepared to finance
Davidson's first effort, let alone his second.

Notwithstanding all the problems, the locomotive was taken
out of the carriage shed on 22 September 1842 and, on its one and
only trial run, reached a speed of upwards of four miles an hour
over a distance of 1.5 miles, witnessed by a 'number of gentlemen
many of whom were noted for their scientific knowledge.'[143]
Unfortunately we do not know who these observers were, and
apart from a few brief newspaper reports, no other records of the
event seem to have survived.

What power might this six-ton locomotive have developed?
If we take the rolling resistance per ton for a railway vehicle as
about 9 lbs per ton, then we can calculate that the horsepower
required to drive Davidson's locomotive at four miles per hour
on the level – ignoring wind resistance – would have been about
0.4 HP. If we assume that the railway was not absolutely level,
then a gradient of 1/250 would double the required horsepower.
It is reasonable to assume that during the trials, the locomotive
developed about 0.75 HP at the wheels. Had the structure been
stronger, the motors would have been able to develop more
torque for less current at any given speed. With a suitable series
arrangement of the batteries, a higher top speed and greater range

would have been achieved, provided that additional current switching problems had not occurred with greater frequency of current commutation. What seems strange is that Davidson adopted direct drive: smaller, higher speed motors, with belt or gear drive would probably have been more effective. But then, he was trying to see what relationship there was between size and power, and it would be many years before anyone was able to define how a machine's power output depended upon its speed, linear dimensions and the magnetic and electric loadings of its magnetic circuit. Given a more solid frame, the use of larger wheels would have also increased top speed for a given motor rpm.

Sadly, the trial on the railway did not result in any financial help, and shortly afterwards Davidson left Edinburgh for London. Rettie says that when he came to Edinburgh on an unspecified date around September/October 1842 to look for him:

> Davidson was gone, and I was told, to my surprise, that after he had laboured for such a time and put his talents and time into operation the parties who had employed him NOBLY PAID HIM WITH A FEW POUNDS ... thinking they did well if they paid him the material. I felt so hurt that I intended to have written him concerning the circumstances, but I did not know where he had gone until I saw your last number.[144]

1. Broad Street in late 19C before buildings were pulled down to make way for Marischal College (Copyright Aberdeen Journal)

'The gable shaped old Water House with huge clock face and urn ornaments was erected in 1766 to contain the water gathered in the Gilcomston and Fountainhall districts. This was the first systematic attempt to bring an adequate water system into the town.' – Bon Accord March 17, 1905, page 6.

To the right of the Water House is a castellated house and to the right of that the large tenement building where the young Lord Byron and his mother lived.

2. The Old Grammar School, Aberdeen
(Aberdeen Public Libraries)

3. Marischal College pre 1836
(Aberdeen Public Libraries)

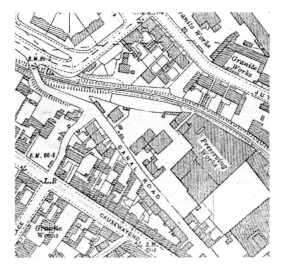

4. Ordinance Survey 1926

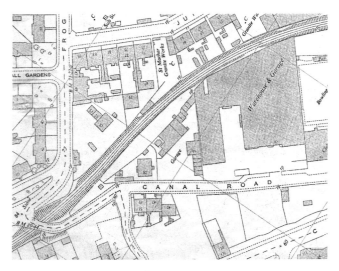

5. Ordinance Survey 1968

6. Remains of Davidson's works on Canal Road Aberdeen in the mid 1970s (Copyright A. F. Anderson)

7. Remains of Davidson's works on Canal Road Aberdeen in the mid 1970s (Copyright A. F. Anderson)

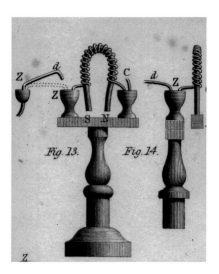

8. Sturgeon's Electromagnet 1824
(Transactions of the Society of Arts, Manufactures &
Commerce Vol XLIII 1825 Plate 3, Fig 13)

9. Henry's 'Yale' Electromagnet Magnet
(USNM 181343; Smithsonian photo 13346)

10. Jacobi's Electro-Motor
(Figure 666 from Wormell's Electricity in the
Service of Man, Cassell and Co. Ltd 1893)

11. The Rev. Patrick Forbes
(Plate facing page 44 in Findlay, A. 'The teaching of Chemistry in the
Universities of Aberdeen' Aberdeen University Press 1925)

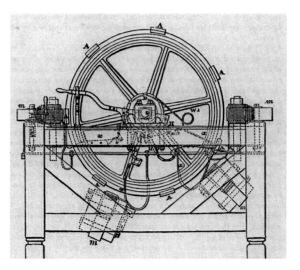

12. Taylor's Motor from *Mechanics Magazine*
(Saturday, 9 May 1840)

13. The Lemon Tree Tavern
where the Aberdeen Philosophical Society used to meet
(Aberdeen City Libraries)

14. Andrew Fyfe

15. Invitation to Davidson's Edinburgh Exhibition 14 April 1842
(Archives of the Royal Scottish Society of Arts [RSSA],
National Library of Scotland)

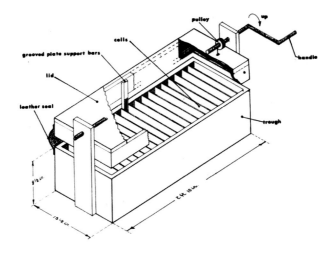

16. Davidson's Battery Zinc Iron Battery
(Based on written description in RSSA Archives,
National Library of Scotland. Copyright A. F. Anderson)

17. Davidson's Edinburgh Exhibition 1841–2
(RSSA Archives, National Library of Scotland)
Presented to the Library by the Davidson family

18. Exhibition Ticket
(RSSA Archives, National Library of Scotland)
Presented to the Library by the Davidson family

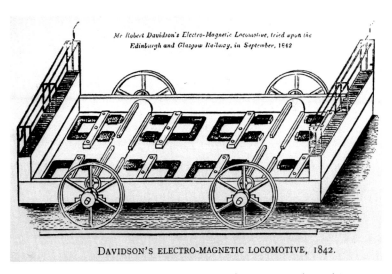

19. Davidson's Locomotive, according to David Mackie
(Practical Mechanic and Engineers Magazine,
Glasgow. Vol II, 1843 Page 51)

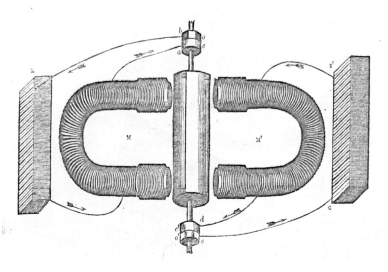

20. Principles of operation of Davidson's motor, from Mackie
(Practical Mechanic and Engineers Magazine,
Glasgow. Vol II, 1843 Page 51)

21. Egyptian Hall Piccadilly 1828
(Engraving by Thomas H. Shepherd 1792–1864. Published 7 June
1828 by Jones & Co, 3 Acton Place, Kingsland Road, London)

22. The Egyptian House, Penzance
A smaller version of the Egyptian Hall owned by the Landmark Trust

NEW MOVING POWER.

ELECTRO-MAGNETIC

EXHIBITION,

UNDER THE PATRONAGE OF THE

ROYAL SCOTCH SOCIETY

OF ARTS.

Mr. ROBERT DAVIDSON of Aberdeen, the Inventor and Constructor of the first Electro-Magnetic Locomotive (which was recently tried on the Edinburgh and Glasgow Railway), begs respectfully to intimate that he has opened an Exhibition, in the Egyptian Hall, Piccadilly, of Models, showing the application of this new power to machinery of various kinds; and of apparatus exemplifying, on a large scale, the effects of the Electro-Magnetic Fluid as a Chemical Agent.

The Models and Apparatus comprise the following:—

1. A LOCOMOTIVE ENGINE, carrying Passengers on a Circular Railway.
2. A TURNING LATHE.
3. A PRINTING MACHINE.
4. A SAW MILL.
5. A MACHINE for communicating the ELECTRO-MAGNETIC SHOCK.
6. An ELECTRO MAGNET. The largest ever made. Its weight upwards of 500 Pounds and will suspend many Tons.

Among the Phenomena which will be shewn may be mentioned the Combustion of Charcoal, attended with a dazzling brilliancy, equal to that of the Oxy-Hydrogen Light.

The Combustion of the Metals, attended is each case with splendid coruscations, peculiar in Colour to the Metal operated upon &c. &c. &c.

The Machines exhibited are different in principle from those of Jacobi, Davenport, and Storer: the whole apparatus, and phenomena shown, will be found far to exceed in magnitude any of the same kind.

and Matters of bad Wefare Scotch Society of ria:

ROOETY OF ARTS.— The undersigned respectfully recommend to their Fellow-Members Mr DAVIDSON's Exhibition of ELECTRO MAGNETISM as a Moving Power, which they may find interesting both to themselves and to the Junior Members of their Families.

ANDREW FYFE, M.D., President.
JAMES TODD, M.D., Secretary.
ALEXANDER ROSE, Couns.
EDWARD SANG.

Open from TWELVE till FOUR, and SEVEN to NINE.

Admission, ONE SHILLING. Children, under Twelve Years of Age, Sixpence.

23. Davidson's first poster for the London Exhibition
(RSSA Archives, National Library of Scotland)
Presented to the Library by the Davidson family

24. Davidson's second poster for the London Exhibition
(Appeared in the Electrical World Vol. XV, 18 October 1890,
No 16 page 276. *Science Museum Library, London*)

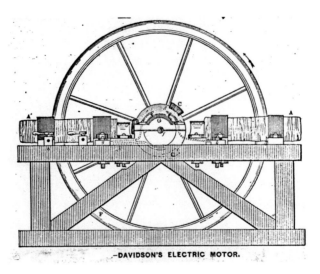

—DAVIDSON'S ELECTRIC MOTOR.

25. Drawings of Davidson's Motor prepared by William Henley
Sent by William Henley to the Penny Mechanic and Chemist

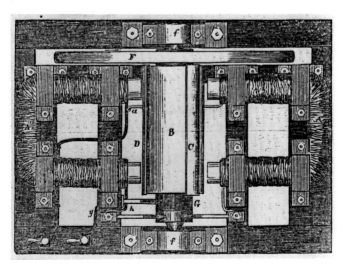

26. Drawings of Davidson's Motor prepared by William Henley
Sent by William Henley to the Penny Mechanic and Chemist

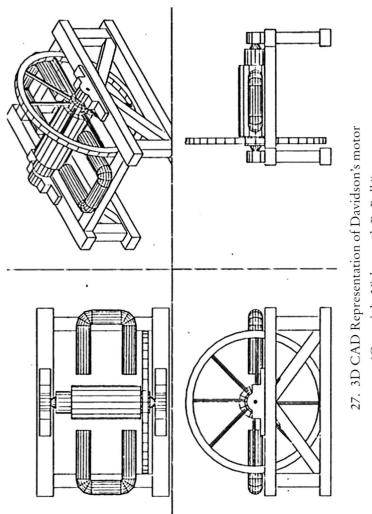

27. 3D CAD Representation of Davidson's motor
(Copyright Vishnawath R. Pullé)

28. William Henley, instrument maker and manufacturer
(Centenary Brochure Page 3: 'One Hundred Years – The Story of
Henley's 1837–1937' by Ernest Slater M.I.E.E., M.I.MECH.E)

29. Robert Davidson of Aberdeen 1804–1894
(Electrical World Portraits – XXV1, The Electrical World,
Vol. XVII, No 25, 1891, p. 454)

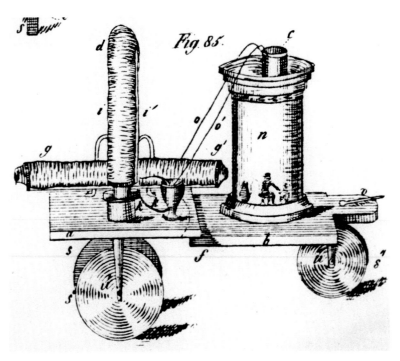

30. Stratigh & Becker's three-wheeled vehicle 1835
(Strattingh, S. & Becker, C.: Ueber die elektromagnetische Triebkraft
und deren Anwendung auf einen elektromagnetischen Wagen.
Dingler's Polytechn. Journal, LXL, 1836 pp. 247–254)

31. Callan's reluctance motors 1837

Callan was a keen proponent of electric traction and proposed using a much bigger reluctance motor than the larger of those shown here. However, he did not take matters further. Both large and small motors are in the Callan Laboratory, Maynooth College, Ireland.

32. Clarke's electric locomotive 1840

33. Colton's Electric Locomotive 1847
(USNM 181577; Smithsonian photo 47048-B.)
Widely exhibited through the northern and western United States

34. Reproduction of Moses G. Farmer's electric train 1847
This was shown at a number of exhibitions in New England during the latter half of 1847. The track was of 18-inch gauge.
(USNM 181348; Smithsonian photo 14588.)

35. Page's reciprocating reluctance motor
with open magnetic circuit, 1844
(American Journal of Science, 49, 1845, p. 133)

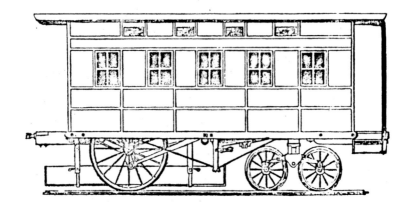

36. Page Locomotive 1851
(American Polytechnic Journal 4, 1854, p. 257)

37. Siemens Railway 1879

Chapter Seven

The 1842 Exhibition in London at the Egyptian Hall

WILLIAM KNIGHT, PROFESSOR OF NATURAL PHILOSOPHY AT Marischal College, Aberdeen records that in November 1842 Davidson 'opened his exhibition in the Egyptian Hall Piccadilly where I and his real friends advised him to proceed in 1838.'[145] Davidson, by this account, had lost much valuable time in fruitless efforts in Aberdeen and Edinburgh, so would it now be too late for him to recover his fortunes?

We must imagine him packing up his belongings in haste – leaving his locomotive to fare as best it might in the carriage shed of the Railway Company in Edinburgh – and making the journey by sea from the port of Leith to London. With him was Mr Sim, who was presumably the same young assistant from Aberdeen who had helped him build his locomotive.[146]

He went to London, as he explained to William Henry Fox Talbot, to open an exhibition: 'for the purpose of realizing a little of the outlay which I have been at in perfecting my invention.'[147] Deep down, he probably realised that the railway companies were not to be won over and all he could do was to try to make the most of things. Shaken by his recent experiences, he possibly hoped that London would welcome him as it has those earlier alumni of Marischal College who made their name in London, such as the physicist Neil Arnott, and William Ritchie the experimental electromagnetician. He settled in rooms in the house of a tailor, Mr Finn of George Street, off Portman Square[148] and set about organising an exhibition. Soon he wrote to his mother and elder brother William in Aberdeen to say that he had fixed on an exhibition room at the Egyptian Hall in Piccadilly. This letter and Davidson's other letters have not survived. However, some of his mother's and brother William's letters survived amongst a package of letters and papers that were donated to the National Library of Scotland by one of his great-grandsons in the 1970s. Replying to one of his letters on 24 November 1842 his mother wrote: 'Dear Robert, trust in God you will be successful in it, we will be anxious to hear when you begin.' She goes on to say, with unaffected pride, that his sister Mary, who has just given birth to a baby daughter, has had a fine recovery. 'Plenty of milk and no trouble with her Nipels and a fine stout contented child I told her how happy you was (sic) to hear of her and her little daughter. She said she was sure you would be anxious about her and she bade me send her kind love to you.'[149]

The Egyptian Hall has long since disappeared from Piccadilly. At that time it stood on the south side of the street almost opposite to the Burlington Arcade and only a short walk from the Royal Institution in Albermarle Street. It was noted for its strange and ornate facade, which took the form of a mock

Egyptian Temple. The Egyptian House in Penzance is an almost exact copy, but to a smaller scale. Above the entrance were two large figures of the goddesses Isis and Osiris, which were said at the time to be 'not very picturesque in effect'.[150] In its earlier days, The Egyptian Hall had served as the home of Mr Bullock's Museum of Natural History, where the fashionable public were able to see a large collection of stuffed animals crowded into what was supposed to be an approximation of a tropical forest. By 1842 the Hall had changed hands several times. The animals had long since disappeared and it was beginning to lose some of its pretensions to being a place of serious and respectable entertainment. Before long it would become associated in the public mind with the spectacular and the odd.

The exhibitions held during the 1840s make an interesting list: The Ung Ka Puti, or Active Gibbon from Sumatra (1842); The Grand Centrifugal Railway and The Remains of a Mammoth (1842); Fourteen North American Indians (1844), who on tiring of the Egyptian Hall, completed their stay in London by encamping on Lord's Cricket Ground; finally, Rock Band Concerts, given by 'the original Monstre Stone Band invented by Messrs Richardson and Sons after 13 years incessant labour and application from the rocks dug out of the mighty Skiddaw in Cumberland'. Some of these exhibitions would have occupied the entire Hall, whereas others may have only taken up perhaps one side gallery. It seems likely that Davidson had some competition from elsewhere in the building during the time that he occupied the Egyptian Hall.[151]

Davidson opened his exhibition at the end of November 1842 and enlisted the help of Peter Gray, an acquaintance from earlier days in Aberdeen who had recently moved to London, to make plates for a handbill.[152, 153] Gray was a fellow of the

Royal Astronomical and Royal Microscopical Societies and contributed on mathematical matters to the Mechanic's Magazine and would have been a useful connection. He is known to have taken up wood engraving for a time[154] and may also have been instrumental in designing the plates for the second and much grander poster. Subsequently, copies of each of the above-mentioned posters were printed by Davidson on his electrically-driven printing press.

Davidson had few visitors at first. Even his 'respectful intimations' in the advertisement columns of the Times that he would magnetise knives and scissors gratis[155] did not draw the crowds. The Times and the Illustrated London News seem to have ignored Davidson's exhibition. However, the Athenaeum wrote:

> The exhibition will be interesting to young persons; but as an application of the new motive power on a large scale we were disappointed. It is very true that sufficient power is generated to draw a small carriage, but surely Jacobi did more, who navigated a vessel on the Neva with a party of twelve or fourteen people on board. [156]

The Morning Advertiser of 7 December 1842 was more generous. The reporter said that the exhibition was remarkably interesting:

> The existence of electromagnetic power has been on many occasions shown; but though there is the power there is wanting the means of so economically applying it as, for instance, to supersede steam. Mr Davidson's models very curiously illustrate to the

eye – for there you see them in motion at the Egyptian Hall – the Electromagnetic Power, working a printing press, drawing a carriage on a railway and propelling a sawmill. There they are actually at work. Mr D's press worked for us the prospectus of his exhibition; he set off his railway carriage, himself being whisked along thereon; and his sawmill severed several pieces of wood almost as quickly as he could apply them to the saw...[157]

The Railway Times, on 10 December 1842, urged 'all persons interested in railways, more especially upon Railway Directors and Engineers, to pay a visit to the Egyptian Hall, and judge for themselves. We can promise them that at least they will feel greatly interested in witnessing Mr Davidson's experiments...'[158] They promised to take an early opportunity to describe the exhibition more fully, but they never did.

The fullest description of the exhibition appeared in the Mining Journal and Railway and Commercial Gazette of 3 December 1842.[159] From this we discover that Davidson placed his battery at a distance of about forty feet from the experiments that he was carrying out and that the current was controlled by lowering or raising the pairs of zinc and iron plates within the battery trough. His electromagnet was large, with square poles, four inches by four inches, and the core was made up of lengths of iron two inches square banded together. (The subdivision of the iron, as we now know, would have hindered eddy currents and assisted the rapid changing of flux with changing current.) His railway was circular and about twelve feet in diameter. His demonstrations of the combustion of metals and a primitive arc light are described: 'From the union of two pieces of common coke a light is elicited of such powerful brilliancy that the eye cannot bear its intensity but for a second or two, and which alone may, perhaps, hereafter be brought into use...' It is interesting to speculate whether Davidson took precautions to shield his own eyes, for if he did not, he must surely have seriously damaged his eyesight in the course of his daily demonstrations.

Davidson, after a good start in his correspondence home, began to lapse; leaving matters to Mr Sim, who was a frequent letter writer. A number of these letters from Mr Sim reached Davidson's anxious family in Aberdeen before things began to get better in London. The family took steps to counter Davidson's evident depression, as we see from William Davidson's letter to Robert Davidson of 1 February 1843:[160]

> I was happy to see by Mr Sim's esteemed favour that things were rather better – and that the two bottles had arrived safe and sound. I can easily conceive what a treat a right good dram is to a scotsman in London. I suppose you have seen nothing good in that way since you went there... I always thought that you would get on in London and now I feel that things will improve... you have great patience, but I trust you will have your reward.

William then offers some brotherly advice:

> I hope you are keeping your outward man in genteel order and that you will not grudge yourself some smart new clothes – let your visitors be high or low it strikes me that this is of consequence – and to the people coming in carriages it is of great importance – and I

hope that you will not neglect it – nor to anything that
will add to the respectability of your exhibition.

His mother was less concerned about giving advice and more
about sustaining the inward man: she sent some fish and a piece
of fine cheese. She was even proposing to make some marmalade
to send, in case he might have need of 'any little relish in the
mornings'.[161]

In William's letter to Robert dated 28 January 1843[162] there
is a brief – and none too complimentary – reference to Chartist
agitators gathering their followers in barns. William disapproved
of such goings-on and calls the Chartists 'cattle'. Their mother's
health is a cause for concern:

> She is at Mrs— at tea tonight. she is fond of a tea party,
> though there are many things better for her... I hope
> she will be none the worse. I am glad to say that her
> cold is better. I can date it distinctly from her having
> been at three tea parties three nights running in very
> bad weather...

A few days later he writes:

> Throughout last night one of the worst gales that we
> have had for many a day. A great deal of lead has been
> blown from the roofs of the houses – roof windows
> knocked in and so on – fortunately we have escaped
> without the loss of a single tyle – though the lead that
> covers the porch of the house that is built on the end of
> ours was laying in Canal Road in the morning. I have
> not heard of any losses by sea though it must have been

a fearful night. Helen awakened me between 1 and 2 o'clock and I never got to sleep again... fortunately all our craft are accounted for. The Clip and the Sylvanus are here and the William Maitland and Mariner are at Sunderland.[163]

Davidson showed a printing telegraph at the exhibition which was described by the Mechanic's Magazine, as:

> one of the most elegant arrangements we have seen for some time... The letters of the alphabet are marked on keys similar to those of a pianoforte; and immediately on touching a letter at one station the same letter is lifted out of a small box at the other. The utility and beauty of a system which gives nearly all the advantages of conversation with an interval of tens of miles between the interlocutors needs no comment.[164]

A model of Sir George Cayley's flying machine was later included in the exhibition.[165] The precise reason for its introduction is obscure, except that it was at a time when there was intense argument over the feasibility of constructing an aerial carriage capable of carrying passengers to India and its inclusion might have helped to draw in the crowds. Henson introduced a Bill into the House of Commons to form an Aerial Transit Company in March 1843, and the relative merits of Henson's and Cayley's ideas would have been of considerable interest at the time.[166] Perhaps Cayley saw Davidson's exhibition as a good way of publicising some of his own ideas and perhaps Davidson thought that the addition of an aerial carriage might help to pull in the crowds. Whether the model was Cayley's convertiplane

– a helicopter – or a fixed-wing machine is not known. Cayley was a good friend to inventors and one of the moving spirits behind the London Polytechnic Institute in Regents Street[167] and his gesture of help to Davidson is quite characteristic of him.

The description of the exhibition in the pages of the Mining Journal, referred to earlier, aroused some lively correspondence including this prickly response from 'Electricitus':

> Sir – having noticed your description of the exhibition at the Egyptian Hall Piccadilly by Mr Davidson, I am induced to make a few remarks on the subject. I am not a practical man in electromagnetism, but I very much question the existence of a power such as shown by Mr Davidson's experiments anything like sufficient for the propulsion of heavy machinery. I have attended Mr Davidson's exhibition, which is certainly very interesting; but from anything that I have there seen or heard, I am yet unconvinced that sufficient power is at command for any real practical use. Mr Davidson is a sanguine man, and I believe, fully expects that he will succeed in establishing a new motive power, and one which will entirely supersede the use of steam, but he must show something on a much more grand scale than his present experiments exhibit, and something, too, producing much more powerful effects, before any man who pays any attention to the operation of the (at present) known laws of Nature can join in the opinion he advances. As a lover of the advancement of science, and its application to really useful purposes, I shall be happy to see that Mr Davidson succeeds, but

from what I can glean from the observations he makes during his description, I am satisfied he has proceeded much further in his experiments, and has gained more knowledge on the subject, than he wishes his inquiring auditors to learn. I would honestly advise Mr Davidson, that openness and candour will, in the present advanced state of scientific knowledge, do much more towards forwarding his own interests than any attempt to keep up the character of the mere showman: and believing that the knowledge of the power of electricity is at present very imperfect, I hope Mr Davidson will do his best to enlighten society on the subject. I trust that, in so doing he will individually reap a lasting benefit.

Bloomsbury Square December 7th,

ELECTRICITUS.[168]

An 'Advocate of Electromagnetic Power' was not long in replying:

Sir... I am sure your sense of justice will pardon me for obtruding a few observations in vindication of a gentleman so scientific and unassuming as I have found Mr Davidson to be, and who, in coming amongst us almost an entire stranger, ought, I humbly submit, to have received more courtesy than 'Electricitus' has been pleased to bestow upon him. 'Electricitus' is candid enough to admit that he 'is not a practical man in electromagnetism' and yet 'he questions very much the existence of a power, such as shown by Mr Davidson's experiments, anything like sufficient for the propulsion of heavy machinery.' I would advise

'Electricitus' before too confidently hazarding such an opinion, to take warning from a certain learned doctor[169] (whose opinion was looked up to at that time as a very high authority), who, we all recollect only a few years ago attempted to prove the impossibility of a steamboat being able to cross the Atlantic, but who very soon afterwards was glad to escape in one to the New World in order to avoid the penalty imposed by the offended laws of his country. Mr Davidson however is not only blamed for not being able to create power sufficient to propel heavy machinery, but he is also accused of 'having proceeded much further in his experiments, and of having gained more knowledge on the subject than he wishes his inquiring auditors to learn.' I know nothing of Mr Davidson beyond what I have seen of him here, and the highly satisfactory notices which have been taken of him and his monitors in the press of his native country; but I am informed that he has devoted many years of anxious labour to the development of his interesting discovery, and if that is the case, can anyone, I ask, 'not acquainted with electromagnetism,' reasonably expect that he can learn at one exhibition, and at the expense of a shilling, that which has cost the inventor so many years of unwearied exertion to acquire. Mr Davidson propels machines by electromagnetism, but I have never heard that he professes to teach by electricity. If 'Electricitus' has really 'a love for the advancement of science,' and a desire to acquire a thorough knowledge of Mr Davidson's experiments, I would recommend him to visit the Egyptian Hall as often as I have done and, if he does, I will venture to say that he will alter his opinion, both of Mr Davidson and of his exhibition and will find him to be hereafter not a *mere showman* but in reality a person possessed of much scientific knowledge, which he will communicate in a frank and intelligent manner.

AN ADVOCATE OF ELECTROMAGNETIC POWER
St James' Park, Dec 14.[170]

'An engineer' then took up the matter and wrote in somewhat similar vein:

Sir... The very illiberal attack upon Mr Davidson by 'Electricitus' is only such as might be expected from one who, as he himself confesses, is ignorant of the subject on which he writes, but yet presumes to give his unqualified opinion. The results of man's intellectual labour are his own to give to, or to withhold from, the public as his inclination or interest may direct. Mr Davidson appears in public such as he is – a plain, unpretending practical man; he has expended much time and money in experiments, which, if successful, would most assuredly benefit the millions inhabiting the earth. He has succeeded to a certain extent, sufficient, indeed, to convince scientific men that much more may be done; beyond this extent, his means will not reach, he therefore, appeals to the intellectual portion of the community, in the, I fear forlorn, hope of finding patrons and friends, stating candidly, that with apparatus of greater magnitude, and the means of making experiments, he has no doubt much more may be done. What right, I ask, has 'Electricitus', or any other anonymous scribbler, to call upon Mr Davidson to render up secrets, if he have any, which, resulting from the toilsome application of the mind and body, may eventually prove beneficial to him? To be the mere showman is his misfortune, and the shame of a cold calculating community; the sham of those who squander their thousands in vain and frivolous pursuits, and leave modest merit to work its own way through the midst of insurmountable difficulties. As a mere mechanic, Mr Davidson has done more towards promoting this really desirable object than Jacobi and other scientific men have done. If Mr Davidson has any secrets, I trust he will have the good sense to keep them to himself, until assured that he will derive profit from them – publish them at the dictum of such honest candid men as 'Electricitus', the literary drones of society would acknowledge the obligation, by being the first to pilfer his thoughts, and then to condemn his simplicity. I hope these remarks will elicit from 'Electricitus', in his future visits, a spark of better and nobler feeling, and, if he cannot lend his aid in the persuit of truly universal object, that he will, at least, have the modesty to remain silent, on a subject of which, by his own confession, he knows nothing.

Grosvenor Street, Dec. 14th

AN ENGINEER[171]

Wisely, Electricitus did not reply. The lack of support given by the British public to its inventors appears to be a fairly constant factor in the onward march of technical progress.

One early visitor to Davidson's exhibition was William Henley, then an electrical instrument maker and later a submarine telegraph cable manufacturer.[172] Since setting up in business in 1837 he had been occupied making instruments for John Gassiot, wine importer and amateur scientist, for John Frederik Daniell and for Charles Wheatstone at King's College London and for William Henry Fox Talbot, the pioneer of photography.[173] The exhibition must have impressed Henley, because he wrote to Fox Talbot on 7 December 1842:

> I beg pardon, but are you aware that there is a Mr Davidson who has an Electromagnetic exhibition at the Egyptian Hall in the Strand?[174]

It seems that Talbot then visited the exhibition and noticed that one of the motors that Davidson was using to drive an electric saw was a reciprocating motor, perhaps somewhat similar in design to the one that he himself had patented in 1840 (No 8680), a model of which was later built for him by Henley.

Talbot seems to have thought that he was the originator of the reciprocating reluctance motor, but in fact his patent did not take account of the prior art and seems, in hindsight, to be very weak. Furthermore Talbot seems to have been unaware that Davidson had built the particular motor five years earlier and had shown it to all who wished to see it and it therefore represented, as far as his own patent was concerned, prior art. He rushed off an angry letter to his solicitors instructing them to take up the matter with Davidson, which they did as follows:

Sergeant Inn, Fleet Street
January 9th 1843

Sir,

We have received a letter from Mr Talbot the copy of
which we think it right to send you:

*Some years ago I took out a patent for improvements
in obtaining motive power in which it described an
Electro Magnetic Engine of a new kind. I have lately
become aware that Mr Robert Davidson is exhibiting
a model of this engine at the Egyptian Hall, Piccadilly,
where it is employed to drive a small circular saw.*

*As I feel it is incumbent upon me to protect my rights as
Patentee, I request you will have the goodness to write
to Mr Davidson and inform him that he is infringing
existing patent rights – but I only speak of the model
which works the saw, for the rest of the machines are
on a different principle. – at the same time however I
wish to say that it is not at all my wish to prevent the
exhibition of the above mentioned machine, on the contrary I will with pleasure give Mr Davidson my licence
and permission to continue to exhibit it as I believe him
to be a very ingenious man, provided that he will give
me an undertaking not to make any other Engine or
model in the principle of my patent in England and
Wales without written license and permission to do so.*

My patent not extending to Scotland, he will be at

*liberty to do as he pleases there. If Mr Davidson will
refer to the enrolled specification of my patent he will
see that his machine is identical with the one I have
described.*

(signed) W. H.F. Talbot

We are Sir, W. R. King and Son, Solicitors to Mr Talbot.
Our charge for attending Mr Talbot and writing this
letter l0s.6d.[175]

Not only was Davidson faced with the threat of Talbot going to
law and obtaining an injunction to stop him exhibiting one of
his motors, but Talbot's solicitors had thought fit to charge him
for the cost of writing the letter! Davidson wrote a conciliatory
reply immediately:

London, Egyptian Hall, Piccadilly
January 11th 1843.

Sir,

I have just received a letter from Messrs. W. R. King
and Son, purporting to contain the copy of a letter
from you accusing me of having infringed your existing
patent rights by exhibiting the modle (sic) of a machine
which works a small circular saw – and requesting
me to give you an undertaking not to make any other
Engine or modle on the principle of your patent in
England or Wales without your written license and
permission to do so.

If I have in any way infringed upon your patent I am extremely sory (sic) but perhaps you are not aware of the fact that the very identical machine which I am now exhibiting was made by me about six years ago and publicly exhibited to thousands previous to your patent having been taken out. Under these circumstances I am convinced you will pardon me if I am infringing upon your patent and as I have only been exhibiting for the purpose of realising a little of the outlay witch I have been at in perfecting my invention, I hereby most cheerfully undertake not to make any engine or Modle(sic) in England or Wales with the view of infringing upon your patent without your written license and permission so to do.

I am,
Yours most respectfully,
Robert Davidson [176]

It seems that it took a further exchange of letters – now lost – before an amicable settlement could be achieved for Davidson evidently wrote to his brother William to ask him to enlist the help of Patrick Forbes in proving his priority over Talbot and he would not have needed to do this if Talbot had found the assurances in his first letter acceptable. William expressed his own feelings in a reply to Robert on 20 January 1843:

Talbot must be anything but an 'English Gentleman' else he could never have acted in the way he has done – and your first letter was quite enough – in your return – how you were truly to be pitied – and I do not see

how you could have acted differently – as even if you
had been found right at law, he would no doubt have
stopped your mill until the thing was settled – which
would have cost you both time and money besides
much vexation – and want of rest – it is well the thing
is not worse – for really when I began to read Mr Sim's
long letter I was afraid that there was some terrible
develry (sic) pending – and I suppose you can comfort
yourself with the thought that you can plan a better.

William Davidson had evidently been to consult Patrick Forbes,
for he then quoted Forbes' forthright views on the matter:

You have done quite right – and that if Talbot is the
silly vain fool that I take him to be that his interference
will be the best thing that can have happened, as his
vanity will induce him to send all his friends to see
your mill.[177]

At the time, William Grove – inventor of the Grove Cell and
the gas battery (fuel cell) – was preparing a lecture on electromagnetism to deliver before the Royal Institution and he wrote
to Talbot to say that he was hoping to visit Davidson's exhibition
beforehand.[178] We know, from a comment in one of William
Davidson's letters to Robert, that Grove was well pleased with
what he saw. We may wonder what path that conversation
between the two inventors took: did they speculate that one day a
fuel cell might provide an effective means of converting chemical
into electrical energy and thereby provide a powerful motive
force for vehicles?

The Penny Mechanic and Chemist, a weekly magazine

dedicated to: 'the supply of valuable information to the operative and the productive classes, as well as to all lovers of arts and sciences' printed an account of the exhibition by a contributor 'W. H.' the same William Henley, instrument maker, mentioned earlier, who describes – with two scale drawings – a motor with a five-foot flywheel and two electromagnets which ran at a speed of about 50 to 60 rpm. This was the motor used by Davidson to drive a small printing press and a five-inch turning lathe. Henley also mentions the much smaller reciprocating motor with a two-foot diameter flywheel, which drove a sawmill. He said this could cut through a one-inch square piece of wood in one second. Henley's drawings are fairly detailed, probably to scale, and are the work of someone used to analysing a mechanism into its components.

Henley had already built several reluctance motors of different kinds for Charles Wheatstone, so he was in a good position to judge the relative performance of Davidson's machines. Henley came away from the exhibition with his interest in practical application of electromagnetism greatly strengthened. But it seems that Wheatstone, his erstwhile sponsor, had now become a sceptic, because in his letter there is veiled criticism of august professors who have little faith in electromagnetic power:

> ...even professors fingers or arms, either I imagine, would stand a poor chance if in the way of either of Mr Davidson's models.[179]

Nor was the potential of electromagnetic power lost on the ordinary man, as we see from this letter Davidson received from a farmer while at the Egyptian Hall:

Mr R Davidson. I saw a paragraph in the Doncaster cronical transfered from the Edinbro Journal a trial of an Electro magnetic propeling ingen as a substitute for steam constructed by you. I subsequently wrote to a Mr Davidson named in the paragraph and he sent me your address.

Sir, I have long contemplated the subject of magnetism as a substitute for steam but not been acquainted with the nature permit me the liberty of soliciting your candid approbation upon the Nature of magnetism. Can you make a three or four horse power propeling magnet Engen equivilent (sic) to the same horse of steam power plane, and strong and effective and portable. I would attach one to a small threshing machine instead of our horses providing you can construct one of a large size I would apply it to a corn mill to grind corn with your advice upon the object will much oblege (sic) me and likewise a list of prices in order to frame an estimate on my projection.

I read your address from Charles Davidson. Jany 23/1843 Joseph Hollis, Worksop Nottinghamshire.[180]

Davidson's exhibition ran for about six months: he paid his last rent bill of 24 pounds to the proprietor of the Egyptian Hall on 9 June 1843.[181] William Knight wrote in his notebook: 'July 14th 1843. Mr Robert Davidson returned this week to Aberdeen with his Electromagnetic Machines, having succeeded tolerably in London with his exhibition, but acquired no patrons there.'[182] It seems that Davidson covered his expenses in London, but little more. His dreams of finding sponsors or of making a fortune out of electromagnetism were truly shattered.

When Davidson began his work in 1837, the prospects of extracting electrical energy from batteries must have seemed limitless: but experience both as chemist and experimenter must have taught him to appreciate the cost of his raw materials. It was a hard way to discover that the primary battery had limitations as a power source. By 1843, James Prestcott Joule's work in Manchester was just becoming known and the high hopes of replacing steam with battery driven motors was fading. In 1841 Joule had shown that:

> the duty of the best Cornish steam engine is about 1,500,000 lbs raised to the height of 1 ft by the combustion of coal, which is nearly equal to five times the extreme duty that I was able to obtain from my electromagnetic engine by the consumption of a pound of zinc. This consumption is so unfavourable that I confess I almost despair of the success of electro-magnetic attraction as an economical source of power. For although my machine is by no means perfect, I do not see how the arrangements of its parts could be improved so as to make the duty per 1 lb of zinc superior to the best steam engines per 1 lb of coal; and even if this were obtained, the expense of the zinc and the exciting fluids of the battery is so great when compared with the price of coal as to prevent the ordinary electromagnetic engine being useful for any but very peculiar purposes.[183]

Robert Hunt, the scientific writer, expressed the situation in the late 1850s thus:

> Animal power depends on food
> Steam Power depends on coal
> Electrical Power depends on zinc[184]

We take the concept of electrical energy transmission for granted today, but it is doubtful if it would have made much sense to many of Davidson's generation, who had been bred on the idea that a portable primary battery consuming zinc might be a direct replacement for a steam boiler. It was not until Gramme showed in 1873 that an electrical generator could transmit power by overhead line three-quarters of a mile away that the full potential of electricity as a medium of energy transmission began to come clear.

In the future, the primary battery, in the form of the Leclanché cell, would be relegated to powering electric bells, radios and small toys, whereas the bulk of electricity would be generated in huge centralized steam-driven power stations before being distributed to where it was needed; allowing industry to grow in areas where the natural resources of coal and water were absent. All this would have to wait for the development of efficient generators and for the invention of the carbon filament lamp. The electric light would bring electricity into the home and create a large base load. Only then, when there was some spare power available, would Davidson's dream of an electrified railway be realised, and then in a form which he would hardly have recognised.

It is, however, interesting to note that belief in the efficacy of steam was not universal. The Times[185] refers to a conversation between a correspondent, then a young man, and the railway engineer George Stephenson (1781–1848) that took place in 1847, in which Stephenson said:

> I have the credit of being the inventor of the loco-motive. It is true that I have done something to im-prove the action of steam for that purpose, but I tell you, young man, I shall not live to see it, but you may, when electricity will be the great motive power of the world.

The period between the end of Davidson's experiments in 1843 and 1879, when the first practical electric railway was demon-strated in Berlin, is full of interest. The next chapter sets David-son's experiments in the context of the other developments that followed during this period.

Chapter Eight

The 'Nestor of the Art of Electric Traction'

Robert Davidson in later years

ROBERT DAVIDSON LEFT LONDON IN MID 1843 AND RETURNED to Aberdeen a disappointed man. As William Knight wrote in his notebook:

> Mr Robert Davidson retuned this week to Aberdeen with his Electromagnetic Machines, having succeeded tolerably well in London with his exhibitions, but acquired no patrons there. At Edinburgh he lost nearly a year working for the Railway Company who used him very ungenerously. The Society of Arts never paid him the £15 voted in 1841. He speaks with great contempt of his treatment and seems not inclined to go on: indeed for nearly three years nothing has effectively been done on the subject power in the electrical mover being wanted. The slow motion of his engine at Edin'

he ascribes to the wheels having been by far too small: it was left in the Company's hands.[186]

It seems that Davidson remained in Aberdeen for the rest of his long life. For many years he continued in business as a manufacturer of chemicals for various industrial concerns and he used the spare land on his feu at Canal Road for a small horticulture business. A few surviving bills from the late 1850s show that he supplied bedding plants to local firms. Among the plants bought of 'Robert Davidson, Florist' we find: fuschias at 5d each, carnations, phlox, pinks dahlias and pot of lily of the valley.[187]

In October 1890, as a result of the sudden interest in electrified railways then just coming into vogue, the press rediscovered Davidson. Electrical World, the leading American electrical engineering magazine, found out that Davidson was still alive and under the title 'The Earliest Electric Railway' published the first of two articles about him.[188] The article begins:

It is probably a fellow-countryman of our own to whom we must look for the first experimental efforts toward electric traction. Late in the autumn of 1835 Thomas Davenport, a blacksmith of Brandon, Vt., who had, with the enterprise characteristic of American inventors, worked through the patent office a broad claim covering the general principle of applying electromagnetic motors to machinery, turned his hand toward the building of an automobile machine and set up a small model which was exhibited at Springfield Mass. Nothing however, came of this spasmodic effort, and the first electric locomotive of any practical

111

dimensions was the invention of one who to-day is
perhaps the oldest living electrician, Robert Davidson,
of Aberdeen, Scotland.

The article published the poster showing the Galvani that
Davidson had had printed to advertise the 1843 exhibition in
London and an elevation of the machine used to drive his lathe
taken from the pages of the 23 September 1843 issue of the
Penny Mechanic and Chemist. As if to place Davidson's work
in the context of nearly sixty years of electrical progress, the
article is immediately followed by a description and drawing of
the new Westinghouse Street Railway Motor: a two pole d.c.
commutator motor with a surface wound armature, windings
thoroughly insulated and mechanically constrained to the high-
est standard and with the mechanical parts easily disassembled
for maintenance and repair.

The Electrical World article seems to have stimulated Aberdeen newspapers to take an interest in the old man because one
of them sent their reporter round to his house in Canal Road and
interviewed him.

Mr Davidson is, albeit rather frail, an exceedingly
bright old man and he cordially welcomed us when we
paid him a visit the other day. His memory is not by
any means as good as it once was and his powers of
speech have become much affected.

The article – entitled 'After Work: Robert Davidson – An
Ingenious Aberdonian' was published on 21 January 1891 –
reports that Davidson's locomotive was destroyed by jealous
railway workers in the engine shed in Edinburgh and not in Perth

as claimed by Electrical World. It says that he did not pursue the subject further after the locomotive's destruction because of 'the great cost of chemicals and the apathy with which the machine was regarded by the railway companies'.[189]

Davidson's son, also called Robert, showed the reporter through the house in Canal Road and over a shop nearby in which were stored:

> ...a most varied and wonderful collection of articles. Side by side will be found antiquarian relics, musical instruments, electrical appliances, pictures, photographic models etc.

The old man was clearly a magpie for, in among the chiming clocks and Crown Derby vases, the swords and the daggers was a collection of no less than about eighty fiddles, a number of organs and harmoniums and some capital musical boxes. It seems ironic that Davidson himself was unable to play a musical instrument. The scene inside the shop must have been chaotic, because the reporter went on:

> ...he is also a lover of works of art and has stored away in the most careless fashion a number of portraits in oils and engravings, some by Hogarth being among the latter.

As an aside, presumably his family did not share this love of things fine and rare, for nothing seems to have been passed on to his descendants. Nor do there appear to be any records in the local newspapers of a sale following his death and what happened to his electrical equipment and especially his switched reluctance motors therefore remains a mystery. Perhaps some equipment found its way eventually into museums where it lies unattributed and unrecognised. Who knows?

The unknown reporter weaves a fascinating tapestry of reminiscences: how once in the days of the body snatchers, a mob had surrounded his father's house because of suspicions about the activities of the two medical students who lodged there; how on more than one occasion he had had visits from the Inland Revenue, who suspected that he might be illicitly manufacturing Barley Bree (illicit whisky) in his chemical works; how during a cholera epidemic that once broke out in the city he had gone for a while to live in Peterhead; how he had been a friend of Lord Provost Hadden, now long since dead.

Davidson had, it seemed, not spent his later years in idleness. He had taken up photography in its early days and had become a great enthusiast, making all his own materials. The reporter was shown some of his photographs, which he thought were of a high standard.

This is an interesting insight. Davidson's life seems to have involved a progression of interests: from astronomy in the 1830s, followed by the practical application of electromagnetism in the late 1830s and early 1840s and completed by photography in his later years.

The Northern Figaro followed with an article on 24 January 1891 entitled 'Mr Robert Davidson. The oldest living electrician'. It began:

In these days of electrical invention, when we can scarcely take up a paper without finding in it some new discovery or development of that subtle power, it is with some pride that we present our readers this week with the portrait of a fellow-citizen, yet living in our midst, who was undoubtedly the first to demonstrate the possibility of electrical traction in a practical way.

Mr Robert Davidson, who has for more than half a century resided in Canal Road, Aberdeen. Born in 1804, he is thus in his 87th year, and although he has lived in retirement for a number of years, is yet able to be up and about, interesting himself in the progress of this science to which he devoted so many of the earlier years of his life.

The article quotes two extracts from local papers describing his 1840 exhibition in Aberdeen and suggests, incorrectly, that after this exhibition 'Mr Davidson was induced, under the patronage of the Royal Scottish Society of Arts, to visit the principal towns throughout the kingdom with his exhibition'.[190] It repeated the claim by Electrical World that the Galvani had been destroyed in Perth, rather than Edinburgh, and concluded:

Heart-breaking as this outrage must have been to Mr Davidson at the time it happened, yet he has not been left without some compensation, in having lived to see the triumph of the principles he did so much to propagate in the inauguration of the City and South of London Electric Railway by the Prince of Wales a couple of months ago, and we congratulate Mr Davidson on the gratification that this event must have accorded him, even after a fifty-year wait. Want of space prevents us from going further into this matter in the meantime, but we have no doubt now that public

attention has been drawn to it, that Mr Davidson will
receive the recognition he so well deserves at the hands
of his fellow citizens.

And that was more or less that, insofar as the contemporary
Aberdeen public's interest in Davidson was concerned.[191]

In mid 1892, Electrical World published a second article entitled 'Electrical World Portraits XXVI – Robert Davidson'.[192]
It described Davidson as 'certainly the Nestor of the art of
electrical traction' and included a portrait of him.

> In spite of the weight of his years, Mr Davidson is
> even now a bright old man full of reminiscences of his
> long and interesting career. He certainly was one of
> the pioneers of applied electricity, working contem-
> poraneously with Thomas Davenport, the Vermont
> blacksmith, and on a much larger scale. He has lived
> to see the dream of his youth more than realised in the
> everyday work of his old age, and now in the evening
> of a long and useful life he can look back over the half
> century that is gone, and, as the oldest electrician,
> appreciate even more than others the success of those
> who have followed him.

It is interesting to speculate why Davidson made no further contribution to electrical engineering. Firstly, there was the cost of
chemicals for experiment, coupled with the blow brought about
by the destruction of his locomotive. Secondly, there seems to
have been a general decline in interest in electromagnetism as
a potential motive power (1) because of improvements in the
steam engine during the 1840s and (2) because James Joule, the

Manchester physicist, had proved beyond reasonable doubt that motors driven by primary batteries were uneconomic. Thirdly, in 1847 Davidson's mentor Rev Patrick Forbes died. Fourthly, following his return from London there were several deaths in his own family, which must have thrown a considerable strain on him as the remaining family breadwinner. Fifthly, he lived a long way from the major cities of London, Manchester, Edinburgh and Glasgow where other electromagneticians might have been found with whom to maintain contact. Sixthly, he seems only to have had a passing interest in electromagnetic telegraphy, which was the one area of applied electromagnetism to 'take off' in the mid nineteenth century and where he could conceivably have made his fortune. Seventhly, he seems to have replaced an enthusiasm for electromagnetism with new and strong interests in amateur photography and in collecting antiques. Photography would have provided a distinct challenge and interest to a chemist at that time.

The picture painted by the reporters of the 1890s is of an ancient, tranquil, bright-eyed Rip Van Winkle who had confounded his critics and lived to see electric trains running on the City and South London Tube Railway.

The census records reveal that his private life had at times been perhaps somewhat disordered, at least by the standards of those days:

- The 1841 Census lists him as living in Canal Road and, presumably under one roof: Robert's brother William Davidson and his wife Helen, Robert Davidson, Elizabeth Davidson their mother (age 65) and maid servants Elizabeth Brebner (age 20) and Jane Robertson (age 15).

- The 1851 Census lists Robert Davidson and Mrs Elizabeth Davidson (his mother) living at 32 Canal Road and Margaret Ross, housemaid, aged 17.

- The 1861 Census lists Robert Davidson as living alone at Canal Road.

- The 1871 Census lists Robert Davidson as Chemist, unmarried, living at 33 Canal Road and Margaret Ross as living with two children, Mary Davidson (13) and Robert Davidson (4) at 30 Canal Road.

- The 1881 Census lists Robert and Margaret Davidson as married and living at 32 Canal Road.

The facts above suggest an affair between Robert Davidson and Mary Ross at around the time of the death of Robert's mother, circa 1857–8, for Mary was born in 1858. Robert Davidson would then have been 54 and Margaret Ross 22. An attempt seems to have been made to hush up the affair: for either Margaret and daughter Mary were banished from Canal Road in 1861, or their presence was kept from the Census officers. By the time of the 1871 Census Margaret was installed with two children at 30 Canal Road and Robert in 33. In 1873 Robert and Margaret were officially married.[193]

In 1879, as if to put a seal on the marriage of six years and to still any wagging tongues, Robert erected a tombstone in St Peter's Churchyard Aberdeen in memory of his father-in-law John Ross. John Ross had died in 1869 at the age of 70 and therefore achieved this status granted to him posthumously. This tombstone is of the best polished granite and the lettering stands out as clearly as on the day when the letters were cut.

Robert Davidson died on 16 November 1894 at the age of 90, leaving his wife, Mary Ross, two grown up children and a modest estate of £2269.[194] His father-in-law's memorial also served as his own. As a nice gesture of economy and family togetherness it was pre-marked: 'Also his wife Margaret Ross who died ... aged ... years'. Her executors, it seems, either forgot to fill in the details after her burial, or perhaps, she was buried elsewhere...

So let us leave Robert Davidson in the early 1890s, with a couple of years to live, a respected elder citizen of Aberdeen with his family affairs now more or less in regular order. Here, at last, he was finding some small recognition for his part in bringing about the electrical age then dawning: lost in a lifetime of memories and surrounded by a mountain of bric-a-brac, antiques and historical electrical equipment, the latter being all that remained of his labours of half a century before when the 'New Moving Power' was little more than a dream in the mind of the inventor. Looking back, did he regret being too busy with his locomotive to take up Robert Chambers' offer to drive one of his Edinburgh printing presses in 1841? Did he regret failing to describe his motor in his report for the Royal Scottish Society of Arts? Did he regret not developing his printing telegraph further? We will never know.

If there is one lesson to be learned from the story of Robert Davidson, it is that those who wish to be remembered by succeeding generations for inventive genius or their contribution to the advance of science and engineering should not follow his example of being silent witnesses to their own achievements. They should record what they do, both their successes and their failures. They should publish their results to the world as befits useful contributors to it rather than hiding their various lights under various bushels because they feel shy and ill at ease promoting themselves. Engineers! Electromagneticians! Manufacturing chemists! You have to tell your own story because nobody else will tell it for you. Then perhaps, should you be really fortunate, and should rats, mice or floods fail to destroy your written records, your name may pass modestly into the history books.

Chapter Nine

Postscript

Other early experiments in Electric Traction
1835–1879

ROBERT DAVIDSON WAS BY NO MEANS THE ONLY MID nineteenth-century inventor to think of replacing steam power by some other means. In the context of his day, his largely self-funded demonstrator project for electric transport ranks with the electric boat of Jacobi for the ambitiousness of its scope. His experiments took place in the first wave of enthusiasm for potential electromagnetic applications, which occurred between about 1837 and 1843, a time when William Sturgeon was publishing his Annals of Electricity, the first publication specifically devoted to electricity and magnetism, when the short-lived London Electrical Society was holding meetings and publishing proceedings and the first primitive electromagnetic telegraphs were coming into operation.

The realisation that driving electric motors from on-board primary batteries was inherently inefficient and therefore a non-starter stems from the work of Joule, published in 1841, which was becoming fairly widely known by 1843. So it isn't much wonder that Davidson, as it were, found himself carried out on the temporarily receding tide of enthusiasm for electro-magnetic applications. He wasn't the only sufferer: at about the same time the London Electrical Society ceased to function and William Sturgeon ceased to publish his Annals of Electricity. The electric telegraph, although it had been invented in 1837, had as yet failed to convince the public of its usefulness.

The turning point in the fortunes of the electric telegraph, and, with hindsight, for the prospects of all electromagnetic applications, came on New Year's Day 1845. That day John Towell travelled to Slough and murdered his mistress by poisoning her. He escaped to London by train, hoping to lose himself there. Unknown to him the following message had been transmitted by telegraph to London:

A MURDER HAS JUST BEEN COMMITTED AT SALT HILL AND THE SUSPECTED MURDERER WAS SEEN TO TAKE A FIRST CLASS TICKET TO LONDON BY THE TRAIN WHICH LEFT SLOUGH AT 7.42 P.M. HE IS IN THE GARB OF A KWAKER WITH A GREAT COAT ON WHICH REACHES NEARLY DOWN TO HIS FEET. HE IS IN THE LAST COMPARTMENT OF THE SECOND CLASS COMPARTMENT.

The police, having been alerted, followed him to his lodging and arrested him. From then on the public was prepared to invest in the electric telegraph. Even so, it would be twenty years before the public began to see any return on their investment.

Let us now therefore try to place Davidson's contribution to electric traction in the context of his contemporaries in more detail. In this way we will be able to assess the relative significance of his achievement. We will terminate our review with the unveiling of the Siemens and Halske electric locomotive at the Berlin Industrial Exhibition of 1879, because this was the first practical electric railway and marks the start of the commercial development of electric traction.

We should ask: why should anyone want to replace steam as a motive power? Here we need to realise that the steam locomotive of the late 1830s and the early 1840s was quite unlike the smooth-running machines with which we are familiar. Steam power was neither a safe nor a very effective means of propulsion and it had many faults. It was regarded with distrust and did not enjoy that state of semi-sanctified grace that its successors enjoy in the public imagination today.

Firstly, the power-to-weight ratio was low, partly because steam temperatures and boiler pressures were low and partly because the steam was not expanded very effectively. Therefore locomotives could only be used on gentle gradients and this influenced the way in which engineers graded the lines that they built. John Miller, Company Engineer for the Edinburgh and Glasgow Railway, kept the line almost level for the whole of its length, except for the final descent of 1.75 miles to the terminus at Glasgow, Queens Street. Here Miller was forced to tunnel under the Forth-Clyde Canal and used rope haulage for this, the only inclined plane on the whole line.

Secondly, the materials used for building locomotives were poor and boilers, for example, were liable to explode without warning, even though the pressures were low.

Thirdly, the rotating parts of locomotives were not balanced: the practice was first introduced on the London and Birmingham line in 1839 and it was some years before it became widespread practice. The lack of balance caused excessive wear, rough running, occasional derailments and probably explained the flats that developed on locomotive tyres after they had been in service for a while.

Fourthly, smoke from the locomotives troubled passengers – especially those in open carriages – and the hot cinders set hayricks and buildings on fire.

Fifthly, the steam locomotive needed attention, even when off duty, both in raising steam before the start of the working day and in the cleaning out of the ash at the end of it.

Two alternative means of propulsion were devised at about the same time; the pneumatic, or atmospheric railway and the battery driven electric locomotive. Because of the eventual success of the electric railway, the rival but short-lived enthusiasm for the atmospheric railway is easily forgotten. Davidson's experiments took place at a time of keen interest in the atmospheric railway, when the claims made for the system had yet to be tested.

The atmospheric railway – 'the atmospheric bubble railway' to its critics – was intended to overcome the difficulty of getting trains up steep gradients, and the system possessed, in theory at least, an elegant simplicity. Its main features were: a stationary steam-driven pump, which produced a vacuum in a large diameter tube set between the running rails; a moving piston within this tube, which was subject to a pressure difference of a little less than one atmosphere between its two faces, which provided the motive force; a link rod to transmit the force on the piston to the carriage; and a longitudinal seal in the top of the vacuum tube through which the link passed.

The system had some serious disadvantages:

Firstly, no passing was possible. If one car broke down, so did all. But since the same criticism applies to all rope-driven tramways and cable cars, it might merely have restricted its use to certain specialised operations.

Secondly, it was impossible to make a lasting airtight seal for the pipe with the materials available at that time, and speed control – when the seal worked – was almost impossible because of the variations in friction from one section of tube to another. Given a constant vacuum, and hence constant force on the piston, the only means of control was by application of the brakes: loss of braking power, or reduced tube seal friction would accelerate the vehicle. Hardly fail safe!

Nevertheless, on the first short length of atmospheric railway – built in 1840 – it was possible to haul 11 tons at twenty-two miles per hour up a gradient of 1 in 120.[195] This compared well with the average level speed on the railways which, even by 1843, had only reached 36 miles per hour on the best lines.[196] On one occasion in 1843, an uncoupled motive carriage was accidentally set in motion on the Dublin and Kingstown Railway and achieved an average speed of 84 mph up the incline to Dalkey.[197] Such spectacular results must have given the impression of great potential and were quite sufficient to maintain the faith of the inventors and some railway engineers – including Brunel – in the system. How poor the results of Davidson's experiments on electric traction must have seemed by comparison! Those who ridiculed the atmospheric system were likely to view electric traction even less kindly and the proponents of electromagnetic power must have felt that they were ploughing a very lonely furrow.

Sibrandus Stratingh, Professor of Chemistry at the University of Groeningen[198] in the Netherlands, was probably the first person to apply electromagnetism to moving a vehicle. Assisted by Christopher Becker, an instrument maker, Stratingh, who had read about the early experiments of Jacobi in 1834 decided in 1835 to see if he could make a simpler motor that he could put to work. He built a small three-wheeled carriage, which he set in circular motion on a large table, where it ran for about fifteen to twenty minutes, without any appreciable drop in speed. The weight of the carriage, including batteries, was about three Dutch pounds (1.5 kg). No full-size carriage was ever built.

Better known is Thomas Davenport, who, as has already been mentioned, used one of his motors to drive a merry-go-round, sometimes described as a railway, which, with its several carriages, had an all-up weight of 80 lbs (36 kg) When it was shown in London in 1838, it reached an estimated speed of 3 miles an hour (4.8 km/hr).[199].

At about this time (1837), the Rev. Nicholas Callan, Professor of Natural Philosophy at Maynooth College, Ireland, began to make a motor containing 40 electromagnets, which he hoped would have a power output of two horsepower and would be able to propel a carriage of 13 cwt. (669 kg) at 7 to 8 miles an hour (11.3–12.7 km/hr).[200]. Callan's motor was a reluctance motor, with stationary electromagnets and iron bars on the rotor. The engine turned out to be less powerful than expected and no further development seems to have taken place. Much of Callan's equipment has survived and is on display in the museum at Maynooth.

By October 1839 at the latest, Davidson had built a small carriage 'on which two persons were carried along a very coarse floor', according to Forbes.[201] This is possibly the first recorded instance of a passenger-carrying vehicle and demonstrates that, even at this time, Davidson had turned his mind to traction. There is no mention subsequently of a free-running vehicle and so it is reasonable to assume that he converted it into the miniature locomotive that later featured in his exhibitions.

In 1840, Uriah Clarke exhibited a model locomotive at Leicester,[202] which propelled a weight of 112 lbs (50.8 kg), including the locomotive, at 'a considerable speed and for periods of 2½ hours at a time'. The motor used was of the reciprocating type. Clarke does not seem to have taken his ideas further.

Henry Pinkus, an American living in London, took out an omnibus patent in 1840[203] which covered: atmospheric railways; the propulsion of canal barges; electric ploughing; distribution of electric power and electric traction for railways. This patent is interesting because it contains the one idea that makes electric traction possible, namely the separation of the power source from prime mover, with the locomotive picking up power from a stationary battery by means of an extra pair of conductor rails and pick-up shoes. This arrangement removed much of the weight from the vehicle. Pinkus' idea of transmitting power over a distance was lost on his contemporaries, who for the most part were obsessed with the desire for a portable power source, with the battery feeding the motor directly.

There seems to have been a blind spot in the thinking of the day on power transmission, possibly because too close an analogy was drawn between the electromagnetic engine and the steam locomotive, with zinc in the battery seen as a substitute for coal. Better models for a future power transmission system would have been rope haulage, hydraulic transmission or the atmospheric railway.

Henry Pinkus had earlier worked on atmospheric railways[204] and, for this reason, it may have been easier for him to think in terms of electric power transmission than it was for his contemporaries, who had no experience of power transmission in any form. There is no evidence that Davidson thought in terms of power transmission via the track, although one report says that his experiments at the Egyptian Hall were 40 feet from the battery, which suggests that he may have fed the miniature locomotive via the track.

We have already seen that the students at the Glasgow Mechanics Institute were encouraged to enter a competition to build an electric locomotive in 1838, but that no one took up the challenge.[205] In the sessions 1840/1 and 1841/2 the Royal Society of Arts in London offered a premium:

> for any important useful application of electricity to the arts... the Society have in view the probable economical application of electricity, galvanism, electromagnetism or magneto-electricity to chemical manufactures, to the production of motive power and light.

What entries were received for this award is not known, but an award was made to Alfred Smee for his improved galvanic battery.[206] The idea of using electromagnetism as a moving power was in the air, but few people had sufficient knowledge, originality or practical ability to make significant advances. Fewer still could see beyond their own immediate interest in a particular component – be it battery or motor – and think of a power transmission system as a whole.

Meanwhile, in Germany, interest in electric propulsion was stirring and the German Diet offered Phillip Wagner of

Frankfurt a premium of 10,000 florins (£8,000 sterling) in the summer of 1841:

> on condition that he cause an electromagnetic machine to be constructed at his own expense and upon a sufficiently large scale to serve as a locomotive. That a trial be made of this locomotive in order that the Diet be assured of its efficiency and that Mr Wagner be content to abide by the decision of the Diet on that trial.[207]

The Mining Journal later reported that they had received confirmation that Wagner had completed his locomotive and that a committee would shortly be appointed by the Diet to examine whether he was entitled to the premium.[208] Nothing further seems to have come of Wagner's locomotive. The Commissioners appointed to examine the locomotive proposed to the Diet that Wagner should be granted an indemnity of 6,000 florins for his expenses and labour, but the Diet thought differently and gave him nothing for his trouble. The Dutch papers commented enigmatically that 'everybody expected this result of the affair'.[209] Which leaves us completely in the dark as to what, if anything, had been achieved.

In the 1840s, there were two other attempts to build electric locomotives, both American.[210]

Firstly, G. Q. Colton – who had recently graduated from medical college – organised a travelling show to demonstrate the marvels of modern science. To his demonstration of laughing gas and the Morse telegraph, he added an electric motor and then, in 1847, a model electric train. The motor for the train comprised two electromagnets and a pair of iron bar armatures mounted on a rocking frame. The alternate magnetisation of the

ROBERT DAVIDSON: PIONEER OF ELECTRIC LOCOMOTION

electromagnets rocked the frame and this rocking motion was converted into rotary motion with a crank and an eccentric lever mounted on a shaft. The wheels were driven through a large reduction gear. The interesting feature of this locomotive was not its size – for it only pulled four small cars and carried dolls as passengers – but that its power, taken from four Grove cells, was fed to the locomotive via the track. This was probably the first time that Pinkus's idea for power transmission via the track was put into practice.

Secondly, Moses Farmer, of Dover, New Hampshire, built a somewhat more ambitious train, comprising two cars, which ran on an eighteen-inch (457 mm) track. This had a rotary motor and carried its own batteries. The original was exhibited at a number of places in New England during 1847 but was not developed further. Farmer found that his exhibitions did not bring in the expected profits, and he turned his attention to telegraphy, which by then was beginning to demonstrate considerable commercial potential.

By the late 1840s, it had become apparent to all but the most enthusiastic and blinkered proponents of electromagnetic power that there was no future in it unless, and until, a better source of electrical energy than the primary battery could be found. Only in small workshops, where the cost of keeping a steam engine on standby was too great, was electromagnetism justified. Gustave Froment's switched reluctance motor of 1845 is a typical example of a motor driven from a primary battery that could be used for very low power applications. The prevailing atmosphere of the time can best be captured in Robert Hunt's long paper to the Institution of Civil Engineers (1851) and its subsequent discussion.[211]

It is interesting to note the difference in attitude to the

support of technology in Britain and elsewhere at that time. Continental governments were prepared to consider awards to inventors to help fund their projects, whereas in Britain that function was performed by private societies, if at all. Wagner, had he been successful in Germany, would have received his reward. Davidson had to be content with £15 from the RSSA; the rest of his costs he bore himself. Jacobi, as we have seen, received considerable support from the Russian Government. Speculating, it seems to me possible that perhaps the measure of support from Government for advanced technological projects was a measure of the perceived strategic value of technology projects to the state. Perhaps in those states with less secure boundaries, there was a greater appreciation of the potential of new technology in gaining advantage over neighbouring and rival states.

The most surprising example of public funding for electromagnetic transport comes not from Europe but from the USA, and this from a time long after all efforts in Europe had ceased. Notwithstanding the arguments against electromagnetic power which had been widely disseminated, there was one enthusiastic proponent, whose experiments were on such a large scale, and so financially disastrous, that he deserves special recognition for his ability to overspend a Government Research Grant.

Charles Grafton Page should have known better, because it was his job to scrutinise patent applications in the field of electromagnetism. He was well known in scientific circles and made a number of inventions and improvements in the field of electromagnetism.[212] His first motor was built in 1837. In 1842, he took up a job as a patent examiner in Washington and in 1844 he was appointed a Professor at Columbian College. His duties allowed plenty of time for experimentation and, from time to time, he would hold exhibitions of electromagnetism. He was a master of the spectacular demonstration, and his electromagnetic gun could propel a metal bar fifty feet (15.2 metres) through the air. He was interested in the concept of electromagnetism as a motive power and, to this end, developed a series of motors of increasing power over the years. He was fully aware of Davidson's work.

Unlike most of his contemporaries, Page used solenoids with open magnetic circuits, where the return flux path was in air, rather than in an iron yoke. Associated with each solenoid was a long moveable iron core, which was drawn into the middle of the solenoid when current was allowed to flow. With a long iron core, the return flux path through the air had almost as low a reluctance as if completed with iron. Consequently, the mechanical work that could be done per cycle was approximately the same. However, the main advantage was that the force-distance characteristic of the electromagnet was less steep than it would have been in a more conventional reciprocating electric motor: that is, less force was produced but over a greater distance. It was therefore possible to achieve a reasonably satisfactory mechanical action that could then be converted into rotary action by a crank. Of all the reciprocating electromagnetic motors built, those of Page show the closest resemblance to steam engine practice, with their multiple coils, with iron bars sliding inside them, and their crossheads and guides and the current cut-off mechanisms.

In February 1849 Page had advanced sufficiently far to feel confident to seek public funds for an experimental rail vehicle and applied to the US Senate to support him in his investigation into the possibility of electromagnetism. He was lucky enough to win the support of Senator Thomas Hart Benton[213] of Missouri, who was Chairman of the Committee on Military

Affairs. Page was granted an appropriation of $20,000 to be expended under the supervision of the Secretary of the Navy.

Page's locomotive, as eventually built, had a 4-2-0 wheel arrangement with 5-foot driving wheels and a weight of 21,000 pounds. The overall length was 21 ft. and the beam 6 ft. The cabin was 16 ft. long and could accommodate the crew and several passengers. The reciprocating members of the engine comprised two iron rods four feet long and five inches diameter which were attracted back and forth by a series of short pancake coils in which the currents were commutated, as appropriate, by sliding contacts. The battery trough of 100 cells, each with a pair of plates, one immersed in sulphuric and the other in nitric acid, was suspended between the driving wheels.

The public demonstration which took place on Tuesday 29 April 1851 on the Ohio Baltimore railroad was plagued by insulation failures in the motor coils and cracking of the battery cells. Eventually a speed of 19 mph was achieved over a limited distance, but over most of the trial distance the vehicle only achieved walking pace. Neither of the two problems were insuperable and both could probably have been overcome with a little foresight and more attention to detail.[214]

Page's experiments represent the end of the line as far as reluctance type machines were concerned. It was the DC motor, either with Gramme ring or Siemens shuttle armature, which was to be applied in the first practical electric traction drives.

The first really practical and reliable demonstration of electric traction would have to wait another 28 years until 1879, when Siemens and Halske demonstrated a small electric railway at the Industrial Exhibition in Berlin. By this time all the required elements for an electrical power transmission system had been developed: a stationary electrical power generator, an electrical transmission and track current collection system, a variable speed electric motor mounted on the vehicle.

But Davidson, Page and others were right about the switched reluctance motor in one respect – it is much simpler than other electric motors. The switched reluctance motor cannot, however, be used effectively with mechanical switching arrangements because too much energy is dissipated in sparking when the coils are switched off. It is a very different matter with electronic switching where the magnetic energy stored in the magnetic field at the point of current cut-off can be fed back into the supply with very little loss. Reluctance motors require fewer electronic switching circuits than induction motors and this provides advantages when switched field reluctance motors are used in conjunction with electronic switching.

However, it was only in the middle to late twentieth century that developments in electronic switching devices allowed the potential of the switched reluctance motor, in terms of its simplicity and efficiency, to be fully exploited. The modern electronically controlled switched field reluctance motor is a worthy descendant of its nineteenth-century ancestor.

Author's Note

I FIRST BECAME INTERESTED IN ROBERT DAVIDSON WHEN carrying out research for a PhD in switched field reluctance motors under the supervision of the late Dr Arthur Cruickshank at Queens College, Dundee, then part of the University of St Andrews.

At that time, in the early 1960s, the first semiconductor electronic power switches in the form of thyristors were becoming available and Arthur Cruickshank thought that a simple reluctance motor combined with electronic switches should result in a variable speed motor that would satisfy a number of industrial purposes. It was my task to develop the initial electronic switching circuitry and carry out the experimentation that would prove him right or wrong. I was joined a year later by a Canadian research student Robert Menzies, who completely rebuilt and extended the electronic circuitry. This early innovative work on the development of electronically controlled switched reluctance motors is well covered elsewhere.[215]

A necessary part of any research is to place your own work in the context of what has gone before. So I set about placing the switched field reluctance motor in its historical context. It was not long before I became aware that the switched field reluctance motor had a very long history and that in fact it long pre-dated any wound armature DC machines. It was then that I became aware of the work of Robert Davidson of Aberdeen. Nobody seemed to know much about him, but I put what I could about him into the introduction to my thesis.

The years went by and I moved to Newcastle upon Tyne to work on large electrical generators. In the 1973–4 session I was asked to give a lecture to the Graduate and Student Section of the Institution of Electrical Engineers. Because the work I was doing was commercially sensitive, I had to choose a completely different topic, hence the choice of: 'Unusual Electrical Machines'. The lecture handbill described the lecture content thus:

> Many unusual electrical machines are designed for particular purposes, some of great practical value whilst others are curiosities. This paper takes a carefree stroll down some of the by-ways of electrical machine design, looking at reciprocating and linear machines, electrostatic machines, the electric gun and the motor that wobbles the eyes of the Esso tiger.

> As I had decided to bring Robert Davidson into my lecture, I thought that I had better do some research about him and so I contacted Aberdeen University

Library. They provided me with some useful background information from their records and I thought
that this would be the end of the matter. They then
sent me a whole lot more information, garnered at the
request of Dr R. G. W. Anderson of the Royal Scottish
Museum. At their suggestion, I got in touch with him.
It turned out that he was also Secretary of the Royal
Scottish Society of Arts and happened to be on the
research trail after Robert Davidson, whose name he
had come across in the Society Archives for the years
1841 to 1843.

Dr Anderson later asked me to give a lecture on Davidson to
the Royal Scottish Society of Arts, which I gave in March 1974.
Preparation for this lecture was the spur to doing some further
research. The lecture was getting close and sources of information
had dried up somewhat when, out of the blue, Aberdeen
University Library gave me the name of Mr Sydney Scorgie,
a great-grandson of Robert Davidson. When delivering some
books to the library, he had asked if they had any information
about his great-grandfather Robert Davidson and they noted his
enquiry on a slip of paper. Several weeks later the slip and one of
my letters of enquiry came together and the link was made.

Mr Scorgie didn't have much information himself, but told
me that his cousin Alex Davidson did. Within days, a package
of family letters and other material dating from 1842–3 arrived
from Mr Alex Davidson. This turned out to be fascinating
material from the time of Davidson's exhibition in London
from which it was possible to piece together a little more of the
story. This material is now lodged with the National Museum
of Scotland. Over the years Mr Alex Davidson continued to

research his family history and I owe a great debt to him for all the work that he put in. I am only sad that I was not able to complete the book while he was alive.

The Davidson story is by no means complete. There may be material somewhere about him yet to be discovered. No doubt something will turn up the day after publication! But this is what makes historical research so interesting, isn't it?

Acknowledgements

For help from many individuals and organisations including:

Dr Arthur Cruickshank for setting me off
on the historical trail...

Aberdeen University Library

Aberdeen Public Library

National Library of Scotland

The Andersonian Library Glasgow
(Glasgow Mechanics Institute Records)

The Library of the Royal Institution, London

University College Library, London

Dr R. G. W. Anderson,

The Royal Scottish Society of Arts

Scottish Records Office

Mrs Leonore Symons, formerly
Archivist of the Institution of Electrical Engineers

Mr Sydney Scorgie (great-grandson of Robert Davidson)
and his family

Mr Alex Davidson (great-grandson of Robert Davidson)
and his family

Dr Brian Bowers

Dr Bernard Finn

Dr Robert Post

Endnotes

Chapter One

1. 'After Work: An Ingenious Aberdonian'. A long article in an Aberdeen paper dated 23 January 1891 among the Davidson letters now at the National Library of Scotland. For its technical content this article quotes an article published in *Electrical World* but is of particular interest because the reporter had just visited Davidson at Canal Road. A less extensive article on the same theme appeared in *The Northern Figaro* of 24 January 1891. Most other articles about Davidson drew heavily on 'After Work' for their information.

2. Robert Davidson, soapmaker, 1783–1836. See Burgess Book 11 February 1813–21 September 1830, p. 48: 'The Town House Aberdeen. Cautioner Wm Davidson.' Under Scots Law, a cautioner is one who becomes bound as caution or surety for another, for the performance of any obligation or contract contained in a deed. A guarantor. It would appear that William Davidson acted as guarantor (cautioner) in the case of his brother Robert when he applied to join the Guild of Burgesses of Aberdeen. The Burgess Book lists the Burgesses of Aberdeen. For 'Sale of Soap Works belonging to sequestrated estate of Messrs Robert Davidson and Co.', see *Aberdeen Journal* 27 January 1836, No 4594, Col 3. For matters relating to his insolvency see Particular Register of Sasines 1831–40.

   (The General Register of Sasines is the oldest national land register in the world, dating back to 1617. Its name comes from the old French word 'seizer', which means 'take'. The sasine register is a chronological list of land deeds, which contain written descriptions of properties.It is gradually being replaced by the map-based land register.)

3. Information on Robert Davidson, soapmaker, provided by Aberdeen Public Library.

4. *Banffshire Journal*, 10 February 1920. Description of Glendronach.

5. McCombie, William, *Cattle and Cattlebreeders*, William Blackwood & Sons, Edinburgh and London, 1869, pp. 42–43. Describes the character of James Allardes.

6. Smith, Alexander, *A New History of Aberdeenshire*, 1875, Vol 1, pp. 557–9. Land improvement at Cobairdy.

7. *Aberdeen Journal*, 27 April 1853. Obituary of James Allardes.

8. Blaikie, William Garden, *An Autobiography – 'Recollections of a Busy Life'*, Hodder & Stoughton, 1901, p. 90. A description of James Allardes in old age.

9. *The Kingdom of Forgue – By a Herd Loon*, published by G & W Fraser at the Belmont Works 1903, pp. 8–13. Reference to James Allardes selling whisky in Edinburgh.

10. 'Obituary of the late James Allardes of Boynsmill at the age of 82', *Aberdeen Journal*, 27 April 1853.

11. Blaikie, *An Autobiography*.

12. 'The Kingdom of Forgue'.

13. Davidson, William. Merchant and student at Marischal College 1815–19. Marischal College Records, Vol 2, p. 424.

14. *Aberdeen Journal*, 10 November 1847. Obituary of William Davidson.

15. *Aberdeen Journal*, Davidson, Isobel. Died 30 May 1824 at Mile End Cottage.

16. 'After Work: An Ingenious Aberdonian'.

17. Blaikie, William Garden. 'Lord Byron's Early Schooldays.' *Harper's New Monthly Magazine*, 1891, p. 409.

18. Moore, T. Life of Lord Byron. 1898 p. 6.

19. Masson, D. 'Dead Men I have known; or Recollections of Three Cities'. *Macmillan's Magazine*, Vol 9, pp. 225–227, 326, 331–334.

20. Blaikie, *An Autobiography*, pp. 32–40.

21. Masson, 'Dead Men I have known', *Macmillan's Magazine*, Vol 9, p. 227.

22. Davidson, Robert. Manufacturing Chemist. From Marischal College Records, Vol 2, pp. 435, 442.

23. Masson, 'Dead Men I have known', *Macmillan's Magazine*, Vol 9, pp. p. 227.

24. Ibid, p. 326.

25. Rodger, Ella Burton Hall, *Aberdeen Doctors At Home and Abroad. The Narrative of a Medical School*, William Blackwood and Sons, Edinburgh and London 1893, pp. 92–93.

26. Riddell, James, *Aberdeen and its Folk from the 20th to the 50th Year of the Present Century*, Lewis Smith, 3 McCombie's Court and A. Morison 28 Marischal Street, Aberdeen, 1868, p. 41.

27. Rodger, *Aberdeen Doctors*, pp 92–3.

28. Anderson, William, *The Scottish Nation, or the Surnames, Families, Literature, Honours and Biographical History of the People of Scotland*, A Fullarton & Co, Edinburgh, 1867, p. 683.

29. Reid, John S. 'Teaching Natural Philosophy 175 years ago. *Physics Education*, November 1977, pp. 427–431. This is a modern assessment of Copland's teaching skills and his influence beyond Aberdeen.

30. Copland, Patrick. In *Dictionary of National Biography*, Vol 12, djvu/178.

31. 'After Work: An ingenious Aberdonian'.

32. Knight, William. 1786–1844. In *Dictionary of National Biography*, Vol 31, djvu/273.

33. Aberdeen University Library Archives, Papers of William Knight. Aberdeen have a fine collection of Knight's notebooks and other papers. See also University College London, Archives, 'Apparatus books showing cost of apparatus used in teaching Natural Philosophy Class at Marischal College Aberdeen 1828'. Presented by Joseph Hume. UCLMSS ADD 30.

34. Masson, 'Dead Men I have known', *Macmillan's Magazine*, Vol 9, pp. 331–334.

35. Bain, A, 'Recollections of Dr William Knight. Alma Mater', *Aberdeen University Magazine,* 1889, pp. 96, 97, 106, 107, 116–7, 126–7, 136–7, 148–150, 156–157.

36. Ibid, p. 149, note 36.

37. Masson, 'Dead Men I have known', *Macmillan's Magazine*, Vol 9, pp. 331–334.

38. Riddell, *Aberdeen and its Folk*, p. 49. Knight and the saying of the Lord's Prayer.

39. Findlay, Alexander. 'The teaching of Chemistry in the Universities of Aberdeen', Aberdeen University Studies, No. 112. 1935. This gives an interesting and detailed account of the teaching of chemistry in the two universities and is very fully referenced.

40. Riddell, *Aberdeen and its Folk*, p. 13.

41. Findlay, 'The teaching of Chemistry', p 13.

42. 'After Work: An Ingenious Aberdonian'.

Chapter 2

43. *Aberdeen Journal*, 10 August 1831.

44. Aberdeen Directory 1832–3. The entry for Robert Davidson lists his address as Canal Road.

45. 'After Work: An Ingenious Aberdonian'.

46. 'S. R. Stewart & Co. The Aberdeen Comb Works', The Scotland of Today, p. 72.

47. From a list of entries from the Aberdeen Directory for Stewart and Rowell, later the Aberdeen Comb Works. Information provided by Aberdeen Public Library.

48. Keith, A., A Thousand Years of Aberdeen, Aberdeen University Press, 1972, p. 310.

49. *Aberdeen Journal*, 15 August 1832. Advertisement on File Cutting.

50. 'In Memoriam', *Aberdeen Journal*, 1894, pp. 127–130. Obituary notice.

51. *Aberdeen Journal*, 28 March 1832, 'Yeast for Distillers'.

52. 'After Work: An Ingenious Aberdonian'.

53. Letter from Robert Rettie published under the pseudonym 'Pro Bono Publico' in *Railway Times*, 4 February 1843, p. 136. Rettie was a contemporary of Davidson at Marischal College and was an inventor.

Chapter 3

54. 'Nicholas Callan (1799–1864), Professor of Natural Philosophy at Maynooth College and inventor of the induction coil came from a family of farmers, bakers, maltsters, brewers and distillers.' McLaughlin, P. J., Nicholas Callan – Priest, Scientist 1799–1864, Clanmore and Reynolds Ltd., Dublin, 1965, pp. 10–11.

55. James Prescott Joule (1818–1889) was a British physicist who clarified and proved the dynamical theory of heat and the conservation of energy and discovered the laws of electrical energy.

56. William Ritchie (1790–1837) was educated at Marischal College, Aberdeen. Although he was licensed to preach in the Church of Scotland, he took to teaching. He became rector of the Royal Academy, Tain, Ross shire where, by extreme frugality, he saved enough to be able to attend a course of lectures by Thenard, Gay-Lussac and Biot in Paris. A gifted experimentalist, he became a frequent lecturer at the Royal Institution and Professor of Natural Philosophy at University College London. He died of a fever in Portobello, near Edinburgh, on 15 September 1837. His 1833 paper on 'Experimental Researches in Electromagnetism and Magneto Electricity' contains what is probably the first attempt to investigate he magnetic circuit law. *Phil Trans.* 1833(2), pp. 313–321. Further references: DNB. University College London Archives. Records of Marischal College, Aberdeen. Spalding Club.

57. Oersted, H. C., 'Experiments on the effects of a current of electricity on the magnetic needle', *Ann. Philos.* (London), 1860, Vol 16, pp. 273–276.

58. Letter from Faraday to G. De La Rive on electromagnetic rotations dated 12 September 1821.

59. Schweiger, I. S. C., 'Noch einige Worte ueber diese neuen elektromagnetischen Phaenomene', *Schweiger's Journal* 1821, Band 31–32 pp 35–41.

60. Arago, D., 'Experiences relatives a l'aimentation du fer et de l'acier par l'action du courant electrique', *Annales de Chimie et de Physique*, 1820, Vol 15 pp. 93–103.

61. Sturgeon, W., 'Improved Electromagnetic Apparatus', *Transactions of the Society of Arts, Manufactures and Commerce*, 1825, Vol XLIII, pp. 37–52 and plates 3 and 4.

62. Henry, J. Letter to Benjamin Silliman, Sr. 28 March 1831. Papers of Joseph Henry, Smithsonian Institution Press, 1972, edited by Nathan Reingold, Vol. 1, p. 331. These collected papers contain a wealth of information in the form of footnotes on every scientist in Europe and America with whom Henry was in contact.

63. Ibid. 'Note on magnetic separation', pp. 340–1. Reingold is of the opinion that Henry's use of an electromagnet to magnetise the permanent magnets of an iron ore separator at Penfield and Taft's plant is the first industrial application of electricity.

64. Thompson, S. P., Dynamo Electric Machinery, 5th Edition, Revised, London, 1896, p. 115. This discusses the background to the development of understanding of the magnetic circuit. For a discussion of why Edison used long magnets, see Kapp, G., *Electric Transmission of Energy and its Transformation, Subdivision, and Distribution*, Whittaker & Co., London, 1886, p. 103.

65. Henry, J., 'On reciprocating motion produced by Magnetic Attraction and Repulsion', *American Journal of Science*, 1831, Vol 20, pp 340–3.

66. King, James W., *The development of Electrical Technology in the 19th Century: 1. The Electrochemical Cell and the Electromagnet*, U.S. National Museum Bulletin 228. Smithsonian Institution, Washington D.C., 1962. See also Bowers, B., A History of Electric Light and Power, Peter Peregrinus, 1982, p. 44, and Sturgeon, W., *Annals of Electricity*, Sherwood, Gilbert, and Piper and Gilbert, London, Vol 3., 1839, pp. 429–439.

67. King, *The development of Electrical Technology*, p. 240–241. King gives a very full treatment of the early development of the battery.

68. Ibid, p 241.

69. Daniell, J, 'Frederic: On Voltaic Combinations', *Phil Trans.*, 1836, Vol 126, pp. 107–124.

70. Bowers, B., *Sir Charles Wheatstone FRS 1802–1875*, HMSO, 1975, pp. 140–1.

71. Raby, K., 'On getting the right answer.' Paper 1562A delivered before the IEE Science, Education and Technology Division, 15 October 1981.

72. Ohm. G. S., *Die Galvanische Kette mathematisch bearbeitet von Dr G. S. Ohm*, T. H. Riemann, Berlin, 1827. M. H. Jacobi in his paper 'On the application of Electromagnetism to the Movement of Machines', published in Potsdam in 1835, uses Ohm's Theory. Jacobi's paper was published in Taylor's *Scientific Memoirs*, 1837, Vol 1, pp. 503–540 and he succinctly states Ohm's theory on pp. 511–513. According to Bowers (p. 88) Wheatstone had read Ohm's work and was in a position to have it brought to the knowledge of English-speaking scientists. Wheatstone was a member of the committee appointed by the British Association in 1838 to 'superintend the Translation and Publication of Foreign Scientific Memoirs'. The English translation of Ohm's paper appeared in *Taylor's Scientific Memoirs*, 1841, Vol. 2, pp. 401–506.

73. Ritchie, 'Experimental Researches in Electromagnetism'.

74. Artefacts from the Malay Peninsular made from gutta-percha – a hard insulating material made from the coagulated latex of the gutta percha tree – were first exhibited at the Royal Society of Arts in London in 1843. Gutta percha soon found wide use as an electrical insulation, especially in cable manufacture.

75. *The Collected Papers of Joseph Henry*, edited by Nathan Reingold, Smithsonian Institution Press, Washington, 1975, Vol 1 p. 401. Henry, writing to Edward Hitchcock on 27 January 1832, describes how a tolerably ingenious artist, with some care, would find no very great difficulty in constructing a large electromagnet similar to his Yale magnet. Various methods of covering magnet wire with silk, cotton thread or a varnish composed of Gum Lac and Mastic are described.

76. Francis, G. 'On covering wire with thread', Sturgeon's *Annals of Electricity*, 1838, Vol 2, p. 396.

77. Henry, Joseph, 'On a Reciprocating Motion Produced by Magnetic Attraction and Repulsion', *Sillimans Journal*, 1831, 20, pp.340–343.

78. Wormell, R., Electricity in the Service of Man, Cassel, London, 1890, p 630–31. Wormell does not mention Henry's motor and dates Salvatore da Negro's oscillating motor as 1830. Other authorities give the date as 1831.

79. Sturgeon, 'Description of an Electro-Magnetic Engine for Turning Machinery', *Annals of Electricity*, 1836, Vol 1, pp 75–78. Sturgeon claimed

that he had built an electric motor in the autumn of 1832 and had demonstrated it in March 1833.

80. King, *The development of Electrical Technology*, p 263.

81. 'The dynamic application of the electro-magnetic influence', *Mechanic's Magazine*, 1833, Vol 19 (1 June), pp. 137–8. For a discussion of '.' and 'P. M.' see also Mahr, O., *Die Entstehung der Dynamomaschine*, Springer Verlag, 1941. pp. 21–3, and McLaughlin, P. J., 'Some Irish Contemporaries of Faraday and Henry', *Proc. Royal*, Irish Academy, Vol 64, Section A, No. 2, pp. 19–22.

82. Jacobi, M. H., 'A New Electromagnetic Apparatus.' *Journal général des Sociétés et Travaux scientifiques de la France et de l'Étranger*, December 2, 1834, 2, pp. 394–395, quoted in Count T. H. Du Moncel and Frank Geraldy, *Electricity as a Motive Power*, translated and edited with additions by C. J. Wharton, E & F. N. Spon, London & New York, 1883, pp. 44–5.

83. Jacobi., 'On the Application of Electromagnetism to the Movement of Machines'. (Another translation of this paper appeared in Sturgeon's *Annals of Electricity*, 1836, Vol 1, p. 408ff. This is probably the first reference to Ohm's law to appear in English.)

84. The Papers of Joseph Henry, Vol 2, p. 416–7. Letter from Stephen Van Rensslaer to Joseph Henry dated 29 June 1835 concerning Thomas Davenport, and a following biographical note.

85. King, *The development of Electrical Technology*, pp. 263–5, quoting Walter R. Davenport, Biography of Thomas Davenport, Montpelier, Vermont, 1929.

86. Fahie, J. J., 'James Bowman Lindsay, Electrician, Astronomer, Linguist 1799–1862', *The Electrical Engineer*, 6 January 1899, pp. 21–2 and 13 January 1899, pp. 51–55. See also Millar, A. H., James Bowman Lindsay and other pioneers of invention, Malcolm Macleod, Dundee, 1925.

87. 'American Electromagnetic Engine', *Mechanic's Magazine*, Vol 26, p. 416, 25 February 1837.

88. Chambers, R., 'The Electromagnetic Power', *Edinburgh Journal*, 1837, pp. 218–9. This is quoting the *American Journal for Science* for April 1837.

89. *Mechanic's Magazine*, 18 August 1838 Vol 29, p. 336. A description of a model of a locomotive engine now exhibiting at the Adelaide Gallery.

90. 'Electromagnetic Engines', *Mechanic's Magazine*, 29 February 1840, Vol 32, p. 407. This states that the MM has just received from New York the second number of a newspaper bearing the title of the Electro Magnet, and Mechanics Intelligencer, dated 25 January 1840, published by Davenport, containing the announcement that it is printed on a press propelled by electro magnetism. See also 'Davenport's Electro-magnetic Engine', from the American correspondent of the *Morning Herald, Mechanic's Magazine*, 9 September 1837, Vol 27, pp. 404–5,

91. *Mechanic's Magazine*. Vol 28, 1838 p. 166. Letter from T. Oxley in reply to 'F' on the subject of Davenport's Motor. Davenport's claims aroused some lively correspondence in the magazine, which drew attention to the work of Callan, Jacobi and others. The fact of the matter is: no one can claim priority for the invention of the electric motor. It represents a good example of parallel invention.

92. *Franklin Journal*, January, 1838.

93. 'Magnetic Moving Power', *Mechanic's Magazine*, 3 March 1838, Vol 28, p. 384.

94. *Minutes of the Glasgow Mechanic's Institute*. Prizes offered for the Session 1838–9. From the Archives Department, Andersonian Library, University of Strathclyde.

95. Mackie, D. Letter to John Leadbetter, President of the Mechanic's Institute dated 30 April 1839, *GMI Records*, Archives Department, Andersonian Library, University of Strathclyde. Mackie was later to write a paper describing Davidson's electric locomotive. Leadbetter was the Chairman of the Edinburgh and Glasgow Railway.

96. Jacobi, M. H. Letter to Michael Faraday dated 21 June 1839. The Selected Correspondence of Michael Faraday, Cambridge University Press 1972, Vol 1, 1812–1848, pp. 343–6.

97. Faraday, M. Letter to M. H. Jacobi, dated 17 August 1839, ibid, p. 347. Note. The SS *Great Western* was the first steamship to ply regularly across the Atlantic and was designed by Isambard Kingdom Brunel.

98.   Forbes, Rev. Dr. Patrick. Letter to Michael Faraday dated 7 October 1839 and published in the *Phil. Mag.*, Vol XV, p. 350.

Chapter 4

99.   Fasti Eccle Scoticanae, *The succession of Ministers in the Church of Scotland from the Reformation*, Hew Scott, Oliver and Boyd, Edinburgh, 1926, p. 23.

100. *Aberdeen Journal*, 12 July 1843.Obituary of Rev Alexander John Forsyth, written by his close friend Patrick Forbes.

101. Rodger, 'Aberdeen Doctors', pp. 246–250.

102. *Aberdeen Journal*, 20 October 1847. Obituary of Rev Dr Patrick Forbes. For further information on Forbes, see 'The Teaching of Chemistry in the Universities of Aberdeen', Alexander Findlay, Aberdeen University Press, Aberdeen University Studies No 112, 1935.

103. Rodger, 'Aberdeen Doctors', p. 249.

104. Ibid.

105. Davidson, Elizabeth. Letter to Robert Davidson dated 24 November 1842. 'You will miss Mr Forbes on the Sundays. But you had taken a long walk last Sunday.' On loan to the National Library of Scotland from Mr Alex Davidson of Selkirk.

106. Forbes, Rev Dr Patrick. Letter to Michael Faraday, dated 7 October 1839. *Phil Mag,* Vol XV, p. 350. Reprinted in the *Mechanic's Magazine*, 1 November 1839.

107. 'Taylor's Electro-magnetic Engine,' (Patent dated Nov 2, 1939 Specification sealed May 2 1840), *Mechanic's Magazine*, Saturday 9 May 1840, pp. 694–696.

108. For a history of the switched field reluctance motor see Electronic Control of Switched Reluctance Machines, edited by T. J. E. Miller, Chapter 2, Development History, Newnes Power Engineering Series 2001.

109. 'Taylor's Electromagnetic Engine', (Letter from Robert Davidson in reply to Ref 110), *Mechanic's Magazine*, 1840, Vol 33, pp. 53–55.

110. Taylor appears to have had a means of advancing and retarding the brushgear, whereas, as far as can be established, Davidson's motors used a fixed brushgear arrangement.

111. Highton, E., *The Electric Telegraph*, John Weale, London, 1852, pp. 66ff.

112. Ibid.

113. Dickens, Charles, 'A Poor Man's Tale of a Patent.' First published in *Household Words*, 19 October 1850, Vol 2, No. 30.

114. Knight, W., Notes on Natural Philosophy, Vol 3 M143, p. 775. From the Aberdeen University Archives.

115. *Trans. Aberdeen Philosophical Society*, Aberdeen, 1892, Vol 2, pp. viii–x, xix–xxi.

Chapter 5

116. The Aberdeen Mechanics Institute survived and was incorporated in Robert Gordon's College in 1884, thereby becoming one of the antecedents of Robert Gordon's University.

117. *Aberdeen Banner*, 10 October 1840, advertisement.

118. *Aberdeen Journal*, 14 October 1842.

119. *Aberdeen Journal*, 23 October 1840.

120. Thorrington, J. Munro, 'Dr Hamel, Impassive Scientist', *Alpine Journal*, November 1951, Part 283, pp. 169–175.

121. According to one reference in a Russian encyclopaedia : 'In 1840–41 he found a lot of ichthyolites (fossilised fish) in the North of Scotland and sent some of them to the academy in St Petersburg. He then went to France and then returned to Russia.'

122. Thorrington, 'Dr Hamel', p. 174.

123. *Aberdeen Banner*, 14 November 1840.

124. *Edinburgh Weekly Chronicle*, 17 July 1841.

125. *Chambers Journal*, 1841, p. 241.

126. *Civil Engineers and Architects Journal*, September 1841.

127. Either Alfred Smee FRS 1818–1877, Surgeon to the Bank of England, or his father.

128. Archives of the Royal Scottish Society of Arts, held by the National Library of Scotland, NRA 29073 RSSA.

129. Campbell, Lewis, The life of James Clerk Maxwell with selections from his correspondence and occasional writings, Macmillan, London 1884.

Chapter 6

130. *Railway Times*, 1842. Letter from a WELL-WISHER, Edinburgh, dated 10 October 1842.

131. Ibid, p. 263, col 1, in referring to a meeting of the Edinburgh and Glasgow Railway Company shareholder.

132. Ibid, p. 2 col 1.

133. *Railway Times*, 1841(5), p. 1313, col 1, quoting a correspondent of the *Scotch Reformers' Gazette*.

134. *Railway Times*, 1842, p. 63, col 3 quoting *The Edinburgh Witness*.

135. Ibid, quoting the *Morning Chronicle*.

136. Ibid, pp. 64, 64, quoting the *Glasgow Argus*.

137. *Railway Times*, 1843, p. 113, col 3, quoting *The Edinburgh Witness*.

138. William Knight. Aberdeen University Archives.

139. *Railway Times*, 4 Feb 1843, p. 136.

140. *Railway Times*, Saturday 24 September, 1842, p. 1012, col 1, quoting *The Edinburgh Witness*.

141. Mackie, David C. E., 'The Prospects of Electromagnetism as a Prime Mover', *Practical Mechanic and Engineers Magazine*, November 1842, reprinted in *The Electrician*, 1882, Vol 9, p. 400.

142. 'W. H.', otherwise William Henley, *Penny Mechanic and Chemist*, Saturday 3 June 1843, pp. 167–8.

143. *Railway Times*, 10 December 1842, pp. 1259, 1260, quoting *the Edinburgh Journal*.

144. *Railway Times*, Saturday 4 February 1843, p. 136.

Chapter 7

145. Knight, *Notes on Natural Philosophy*, Vol 3, p. 775, M143 Aberdeen University Archives.

146. Rettie, R., 'Electromagnetic Power'. A letter to the *Railway Times*, published under the pseudonym *Pro Bono Publico,* dated 10 January 1843. *Railway Times*, Saturday 4 February 1843, p. 136.

147. Davidson, R. Letter to William Henry Fox Talbot, dated 11 January 1843. Lacock Abbey Archives, LA 43–5.

148. Davidson, W. Letter to R Davidson, dated 20 January 1843. From a collection of letters on loan to *the National Library of Scotland* by Mr A. C. Davidson of Selkirk, great-grandson of Robert Davidson.

149. Davidson, Elizabeth. Letter to her son Robert Davidson, dated 24 November 1842. From a collection of letters on loan to *the National Library of Scotland* by Mr A. C. Davidson of Selkirk, great-grandson of Robert Davidson.

150. Honour, H., 'Curiosities of the Egyptian Hall', *Country Life*, 7 January 1954, pp. 38, 39.

151. Additional references on the Egyptian Hall. Davidson's exhibition is not mentioned in any of them.

(a) Guildhall Library London.

Timbs, J., *Curiosities of London*, pp 266–268. Ref SL 0511.

Jenness, G. A., *Maskelyne and Cooke. Egyptian Hall, Piccadilly.* Ref L56.8.

London Playbills – Egyptian Hall. Ref St 556–7.

Wheatley and Cunningham, *London Past and Present*, John Murray, London, 1891, Vol 2.

(b) Westminster City Library.

Survey of London. The Parish of St James Westminster. South Side of Piccadilly, Athlone Press, University of London, 1960.

Archives Box 48.

Punch, 'The Deformito – mania', 4 September 1847, p. 20.

Abrahams, Aleck, 'The Egyptian Hall, Piccadilly', *The Antiquary*, vol. 42, pp. 61–64, 139–144.

Altick, Richard D., *The shows of London. A panoramic history of exhibition 1600–1862*, Chapter 18 'William Bullock and the Egyptian Hall', pp. 231–259 and notes to Chapter 18 on pages 527 and 528. This book has a very lengthy bibliography on the Egyptian Hall.

152.   Note from P. Gray of 15 Hermes Street, relating to printed bills for Davidson Exhibition. From a collection of letters on loan to the National Library of Scotland by Mr A. C. Davidson of Selkirk, great grandson of Robert Davidson.

153.   Gray, Peter 1807–1887. Writer on Contingencies. See *Dictionary of National Biography*.

154.   Obituary of Peter Gray, *Royal Astronomical Society*, XLVIII, pp. 163-4.

155.   NEW MOVING POWER, advertisement in *Times* No 18203, 26 January 1843.

156.   *Athanaeum*, 10 December 1842, p. 1066.

157.   'Electro-Magic Power', *Morning Advertiser*, 7 December 1842.

158.   'Electro-Magnetic Exhibition', *Railway Times*. Saturday 10 December 1842, p. 1273.

159.   *Mining Journal and Railway and Commercial Gazette*. Vol. 12, 3 December 1842.

160.   Davidson, W. Letter to Robert Davidson, dated 1 February 1843. From a collection of letters on loan to the National Library of Scotland by Mr A. C. Davidson, great-grandson of Robert Davidson.

161. Davidson, Elizabeth. Letter to Robert Davidson, dated 30 January 1843. From a collection of letters on loan to the National Library of Scotland by Mr A. C. Davidson, great-grandson of Robert Davidson.

162. Davidson, W. Letter to Robert Davidson, dated 28 January 1843. From a collection of letters on loan to the National Library of Scotland by Mr A. C. Davidson, great-grandson of Robert Davidson.

163. Davidson, W. Letter to Robert Davidson, dated 4 February 1843. From a collection of letters on loan to the National Library of Scotland by Mr A. C. Davidson, great-grandson of Robert Davidson. This letter also mentions a Mr Anton whom Robert Davidson has apparently not been able to see recently. This is George Anton, Corn Factor of London, who married Elizabeth (Elsie) Davidson, his first cousin and daughter of his uncle Robert Davidson the soapmaker and Jane Leslie. Their daughter Jane Leslie Anton was born in London on 14 August 1838 and was baptized in the Scots Kirk. She was later to marry Alfred Satie of Honfleur Normandy and was the mother of the composer Eric Arthur Leslie Satie (1866–1925).

164. 'Mr Davidson's Electro-Magnetic Exhibition', *Mechanics Magazine*, Vol XXXVIII, pp. 250–1.

165. 'The Earliest Electric Railway', *Electrical World*, 18 October 1890, Vol XVI, No. 16, p. 276.

166. Gibbs Smith, C. H., Sir George Cayley's Aeronautics 1796 1855, *HMSO* 1962. See pp. 109–120 for details of discussion in *Mechanics Magazine*.

167. Pritchard, J. L., Sir George Cayley, Max Parrish & Co Ltd, 1961, Chapter 9, 'Cayley and the Spread of Knowledge', pp. 119–132.

168. 'Electromagnetism as a Motive Power', letter by 'Electricitus', *The Mining Journal and Railway and Commercial Gazette*, Vol 12, 10 December 1842, p. 398.

169. This was an allusion to the celebrated Rev. Dr. Dionysius Lardner (1798–1859), scientific writer and self-appointed universal expert, who proved beyond doubt – to himself at least – that a steamship could not possibly cross the Atlantic on the coal contained in its

bunkers. He was soon proved wrong by Brunel and others and was glad enough to use this mode of travel in 1840 to elope with Mary, wife of Captain Richard Heaviside, to the United States. See Lardner, Dionysius, *Dictionary of National Biography*.

170. Letter by 'An Advocate of Electromagnetic Power', *The Mining Journal and Railway and Commercial Gazette*, Vol 12, 17 December 1842, p. 407.

171. Letter by 'An Engineer', *The Mining Journal and Railway and Commercial Gazette*, Vol 12, 17 December 1842 p. 407.

172. Henley, William. In *Dictionary of National Biography*.

173. Anderson, AF. 'William Henley, Pioneer Electrical Instrument Maker and Cable Manufacturer 1813–1882', *Proc IEE*, Part A, July 1985, pp. 249–261.

174. Henley, W. T. Letter to William Henry Fox Talbot, dated 7 December 1842. Lacock Abbey Archives.

175. Talbot. Letter to Robert Davidson, dated 9 January 1843. From a collection of letters on loan to the National Library of Scotland by Mr A. C. Davidson, great-grandson of Robert Davidson.

176. Robert Davidson to Talbot, 11 January 1843. *Laycock Abbey Archives*, LA 43.

177. Davidson, W. Letter to Robert Davidson at the Egyptian Hall, Piccadilly, London, dated 20 January 1843. From a collection of letters on loan to the National Library of Scotland by Mr. A. C. Davidson, great-grandson of Robert Davidson.

178. Letter from William Grove to William Henry Fox Talbot 13 January 1843. Collection: British Library, London, Manuscripts – Fox Talbot Collection. Lacock Abbey Archives, LA 43–6.

179. 'Electromagnetism', a letter by 'W. H.', *Penny Mechanic and Chemist*, Saturday 3 June 1843, pp. 167–8. See also 'Davidson's Electro-magnetic Engine', an undated letter by 'W. H.', *Penny Mechanic and Chemist*, Saturday 23 September 1843, pp. 229–230 and a further figure (Fig 2) in the following issue of Saturday 30 September 1843.

180. Hollis, Joseph. Letter to Robert Davidson, dated January 1843. From a collection of letters on loan to the National Library of Scotland by Mr A. C. Davidson, great-grandson of Robert Davidson.

181. Egyptian Hall rent bill dated 9 June 1843. From a collection of letters on loan to the National Library of Scotland by Mr A. C. Davidson, great-grandson of Robert Davidson.

182. Notebooks of Dr William Knight. Aberdeen University Archives.

183. Joule J. P. Lecture given at the Victoria Gallery, Manchester on 16 February 1841 and quoted in Osborne Reynolds, 'The Memoirs of James Prestcott Joule', *Proc Manchester Lit. & Phil. Soc.*, 1982.

184. Hunt, Robert, 'On Electromagnetism as a Motive Power', *Proc Inst. Civil Engineers*, 1857, p. 397.

185. 'George Stephenson and Electricity'. Letter from G. C. W. dated 4 April 1902, *Times*, 12 April 1902.

Chapter 8

186. The notebooks of William Knight. Aberdeen University Archives.

187. From a collection of letters on loan to the National Library of Scotland by Mr A. C. Davidson of Selkirk, great-grandson of Robert Davidson.

188. 'The Earliest Electric Railway', *Electrical World*, Vol XVI, No. 16, 18 October 1890, pp. 276, 277. This includes a facsimile of the 1843 poster of the Galvani, advertising the exhibition at the Egyptian Hall, Piccadilly, London and an elevation of Davidson's Electric Motor taken from the *Penny Mechanic and Chemist* of 30 September 1843, drawn by William Henley.

189. 'After Work: An Ingenious Aberdonian' provides the information that 'it was not at Perth but at Edinburgh where the machine was maliciously destroyed'. The *Northern Figaro* of 24 January 1891, published a couple of days later, repeats the Perth error: 'Unfortunately, however, on its way home to Aberdeen, having reached Perth, the 'Galvani' as it was called, was found in the engine shed there one morning destroyed

beyond hope of repair. This is said to have been the work of malicious hands, instigated by the fear that it would eventually supersede the steam-driven engines with which they were best acquainted.' Edinburgh and Aberdeen were not linked via Perth by rail until 1849, i.e. six years after the trials on the Edinburgh and Glasgow Railway ended. It seems much more likely that the destruction occurred earlier than this, in Edinburgh.

190.   The 1841 exhibition in Edinburgh was under the patronage of the Royal Scottish Society of Arts. The 1842–3 exhibition at the Egyptian Hall in Piccadilly was undertaken on his own initiative, although his posters claimed it to be under the patronage of the Royal Scottish Society of Arts. There is no evidence that he ever took his exhibition to any of the other 'principal towns throughout the Kingdom' such as Glasgow, Manchester or Birmingham.

191.   It seems from some extant correspondence in the Smithsonian Institute in Washington that his son-in-law, by then living in Vancouver, British Columbia, may have tried to persuade the Institute to put on an exhibition about his experimental work in 1893, but there is no indication that it came to anything.

192.   'Electrical World Portraits XXVI Robert Davidson', *Electrical World*, Vol XVII, No. 25, 1891 contains a portrait and would appear to draw upon 'After Work'.

193.   Source Mr Sydney Scorgie, great-grandson of Robert Davidson.

194.   Personal communication from Mr G. R. Barbour of the Scottish Record Office, 13 December 1974. Estate valued at £2,269. Confirmation granted to his widow, Margaret Ross or Davidson at Aberdeen on 31 January 1895. Davidson was designated as Chemist of 32 Canal Road Aberdeen, his widow being of the same address. Records are in the custody of the Sherriff Clerk at Aberdeen.

Chapter 9

195.   Rolt, L. T. C., *Isambard Kingdom Brunel*, Longmans Green, 1957, Chapter 10, pp. 213–230, for general discussion on atmospheric railways

and Brunel's as a proponent. See, in particular, page 215 for reference to the trials on the Birmingham, Bristol & Thames Junction Railway (later known as the West London Railway) where an 11-ton load was hauled at twenty-two miles per hour up a gradient of 1 in 120.

196. *Illustrated London News*, Vol 2, No. 56, Saturday 27 May 1843, p356.

197. Rolt, *Isambard Kingdom Brunel*, p. 217 and Hadfield, C., *Atmospheric Railways*, Alan Sutton, 1987, p. 110.

198. Strattingh, S. and Becker, C., 'Ueber die elektromagnetische Triebkraft und deren Anwendung auf einen elektromagnetischen Wagen', *Dingler's Polytechn. Journal*, Vol LXL, 1836, pp. 247–254.

199. *Mechanics Magazine*, Vol 29, 18 August 1838, p. 336.

200. McLaughlin, P. J., *Nicholas Callan, Priest Scientist 1799–1864*, Clunmore & Reynolds, Dublin, pp. 73–74.

201. 'On the Application of Electro-magnetism as a Motive Power', *London & Edinburgh Philosophical Magazine and Journal of Science*, November 1839, pp. 350–351. Letter from Prof. P. Forbes of Aberdeen to Michael Faraday, D. C. L., &c. &c. communicated by Dr. Faraday.

202. Clarke, Uriah, 'Description of an electromagnetic locomotive carriage', Sturgeon's *Annals of Electricity*, 1840, Vol 5, pp. 304–5.

203. Pinkus, Henry, 'Applying Motive Power to the Impulsion of Machinery etc.'. British Patent No 8644 1840, pp. 24–29.

204. Rolt, *Isambard Kingdom Brunel*, and Hadfield, *Atmospheric Railways.*

205. Minutes of the Glasgow Mechanics Institute. Held in the Archives of the Andersonian Library, Glasgow.

206. Private correspondence with Mr D. C. G. Allan, Curator-Librarian of the Royal Society of Arts. See also *Transactions RSA*, 1841, Vol LIII, p. 21.

207. *Mining Journal and Railway and Commercial Gazette*, 10 July 1841, p. 222.

208. *Mining Journal and Railway and Commercial Gazette*, 9 September 1843, Vol 13, No. 420, p 291.

209.   *Electrical Magazine*, 1845, Vol 1, pp. 608–9.

210.   King, W. James, 'The Development of Electrotechnology in the 19th Century: I The Electrochemical Cell and the Electromagnet', US National Museum Bulletin 228 Smithsonian Institution Washington DC, 1962.

211.   Inst of Civil Engineers 1851.

212.   References for Charles, Grafton P. include:

Land, J. H., 'Charles Grafton P.', *American Journal of Science*, 1869, 2nd series, Vol 48, pp. 1–17.

Post, Robert C., 'Electromagnetism as a Motive Power', *Scientific American*, 15 November 1851, Vol 17, No. 9. This article reports a lecture by Page in New York and contains diagrams and a description of Davidson's motor.

Post, Robert C., *Physics Patents and Politics – a biography of Charles Grafton P.*, Science History Publications, New York, 1976.

Post, Robert C., 'The P. Locomotive: Federal Sponsorship of Invention in mid-19th Century America', *Technology and Culture*, April 1972, Vol 13, No2, pp. 140–169.

213.   Benton's knowledge of electromagnetism was minimal and his understanding of electrical machines was simplistic: electric motors, he thought, were merely machines which consumed zinc in a voltaic cell and converted it into mechanical power, much in the same way as a steam engine might convert coal or wood. According to Robert Post in his *Biography of P.*, Benton's interest may in part have been inspired by the thought that the electric locomotive provided a potential market for zinc, then regarded as a waste product of lead production, with which it was usually found. The nation's greatest lead deposits were located in the upper Mississippi Valley, to a large extent in Missouri. By helping P. he might thereby be helping the mining industry in his home state.

214.   It is interesting to compare Davidson's problems with those of Page:

Page, so it seems, did not have any problems with forces on the moving armature elements, whereas Davidson found that the motor frame was not strong enough to resist out of balance magnetic forces; and

Page had battery and coil insulation problems. Davidson seems to have had neither.

215. *Electronic control of Switched Reluctance Motors*, Edited by T. J. E. Miller, Newnes Power Engineering Series, ISBN 0750650737, 2001.